STORIES

for

EVERY SEASON

52 Stories for Young Readers

by Verna M. Martin

Christian Light Publications, Inc.
Harrisonburg, Virginia 22801-1212

Christian Light Publications, Inc.,
Harrisonburg, Virginia 22801
© 1996 by Christian Light Publications, Inc.
All rights reserved. Published 1996
Printed in the United States of America

06 05 04 03 02 01 00 99 98 97   6 5 4 3 2

ISBN 0-87813-564-2

Dedicated

To My Parents
Lloyd K. and Lydia W. Sensenig
in appreciation
for their love, guidance,
and Christian example
during my own
childhood.

Preface

Thanks to:

* My loving heavenly Father, for without Him I can do nothing.

* My husband, John H. Martin; my mother, Lydia W. Sensenig; and my daughters, Karen Z. Musser and Julia S. Martin; for their love, patience, encouragement, and constructive criticism while these stories were being written.

* John Coblentz, who painstakingly sifted the chaff from the wheat of this manuscript.

* Carol Shank, who saw potential in my "five loaves and two fishes" and prompted the project to completion.

* Rachel Martin, who cheerfully used her talents in typing, in spite of numerous revisions.

* All of you, whose lives have touched mine with love, prayers, and inspiration.

God bless you!

— Verna M. Martin

Table of Contents

SPRING

1. Joel Discovers the Dark

"Joel, will you please run this plate of cookies over to Grandpas?" asked Mother. She sealed the bag filled with oatmeal whoopie pies, handed them to Joel, and proceeded to pack the rest of the cookies into her plastic container.

1

Joel stared at the bag of cookies he held. He was not admiring their perfect texture. He was not sniffing their tempting aroma. He was not thinking how they would delight his dear Grandma and Grandpa.

Joel was thinking though.

How can I, a nine-year-old, refuse to do an errand in the dark that I'd love to do in the daylight? he wondered. *I don't want to say I'm scared. Janelle would laugh. But neither do I want to go clear across the vacant lot by myself.*

Suddenly, an idea surfaced.

"Mother, think Janelle would like to go along over? She always likes to go too."

"No. Not this time," Mother answered. "It was nice you asked, but she has homework to do. Now run along."

Joel set the cookies on the table, then slowly went to the coat closet and pulled out his heavy winter coat. The warm April breeze did not call for such warmth. But goose bumps were already dancing up and down Joel's arms. He knew how very cold he'd be outside, alone in the dark.

Dreading to go out, Joel sauntered over to the kitchen sink for a drink. He dawdled, thinking about the shadows and darkness in the lot between their house and Grandpa's.

Daddy looked up from his work at his desk. "Joel, didn't you go yet?"

"Not yet," Joel answered. "Wanna go along?" he added hopefully.

"I'd be glad to, but I still have some estimates to make. You must obey promptly. Go now."

There was no way to refuse. Joel picked up the cookies, headed for the door, and stepped into the night. *If only I'd have a dog to go with me,* he wished. He ventured carefully across the lawn.

This night is as black as Midnight, my cat, he thought, *except Midnight has one light patch on her front paw.* "And there's another difference," he muttered aloud. "Midnight makes me feel comfy and warm. The night makes me afraid."

Joel's steps dragged as he neared the shrubbery bed. He glanced to the left. To the right. Behind him. Was anything following?

At that very moment there was a rustling in the shrubs only three feet ahead of him. Something black darted across his path.

Joel wanted to scream, but he couldn't. His feet were frozen to the spot.

The critter, black as coal, shot ahead, apparently as frightened as Joel. Then it turned and came directly toward him.

"Meow!"

"Midnight!" Joel exclaimed. "You scared me! For scaring me like that you'd better come with me the rest of the way. Did I scare you too?"

He bent to stroke Midnight with his free hand, keeping the cookie bag out of reach in his other hand. Suddenly, he stiffened again. "What was that?" he breathed.

There it was again!

But then Joel relaxed, for he recognized the low warbling whistle coming from across the vacant lot. "That's Grandpa!" he said.

"Hello, Grandpa," he called.

"Joel, is that you?" came Grandpa's voice from the darkness.

"Yeah! You scared me. I didn't know what I was hearing."

Grandpa's laughter rippled through the darkness. He

3

headed across the vacant lot and met Joel midway.

"What are you doing, Grandpa?" questioned Joel.

"Taking my evening walk," replied Grandpa. "I enjoy breathing in the fresh air before I go to bed. It gives me time to be alone with God. And I enjoy the beauty of the night."

His last sentence stunned Joel. "Beauty of the night? What do you mean?" asked Joel.

"Where shall I begin? Each evening has its own beauty. Like tonight. Let's just hush for a minute."

Joel listened. He heard a sighing, rustling sound.

"That's the breeze sweeping about the branches of the newly budded maple trees. During the day there are too many other noises to be able to hear nature's music. Then this summer the crickets will chirp their songs. In the fall the owls are hooting, and in winter I enjoy the crisp crunch of walking across the frozen snow."

Amazed, Joel thought, *It wasn't that I didn't hear things, but everything sounded scary to me.*

Grandpa continued. "And there are so many things to see."

"See?" challenged Joel. "In the dark?"

"Certainly," answered Grandpa. "Just watch over there beyond that clump of trees. See that moving shaft of light?"

"What is it?" asked Joel. *Was this some natural phenomenon his science book had neglected to tell him about?*

"You never saw it before? That's the beacon light at the airport," answered Grandpa.

"You mean we can see that here?" questioned Joel.

"Yes," replied Grandpa. "Because tonight is especially dark, we can see it better. When the moon is full, we can't see it as well. The moon and beacon take turns

4

entertaining me. And now look up."

Joel glanced heavenward.

The vast dome overhead was studded with countless twinkling diamonds. From horizon to horizon, stars danced and flickered. Also on display was a sliver of moon shaped like a slice of cantaloupe.

Were all these night lights shining above me while I was concentrating on the blackness about me? Joel wondered. *I never thought to look.*

Grandpa continued. "Joel, God placed each one of the stars. We see some of them He grouped together in special groups called constellations. Over there," he said as he pointed skyward, "is a group called the Little Dipper. Notice the bright star. It is at the end of the handle. Job made mention of Arcturus, Orion, and Pleiades. Those are constellations too, but I'm not exactly sure which they are."

"The stars are beautiful!" Joel exclaimed. "I never knew the night was so . . . so . . . I don't know what to say . . . pretty . . . fascinating . . . whatever!"

"I understand how you feel," said Grandpa. "Many people miss nature's nighttime beauty. Once in a great while I even get to witness a falling star. That's a real show. Then I think back. As a lad I was afraid of the dark."

His last comment intrigued Joel. "You were?" he questioned.

Grandpa chuckled. "Yes. I lived on a farm and had to give the horses hay in the evening. The farm had many outbuildings and they created dark corners and shadows. Each evening I'd run as fast as my legs could carry me to avoid any dangers." As he reminisced, his laughter echoed in the night.

"I know the feeling!" said Joel. "Midnight scared me

5

tonight. She was sleeping in the shrubbery bed, and we startled each other."

Grandpa laughed, then asked, "Where is she now?"

"Right here, rubbing my legs," answered Joel.

"Pick her up and look into her eyes," suggested Grandpa. "They glow."

"First take this bag of cookies from Mother," said Joel as he handed the goodies to Grandpa.

While Grandpa expressed his appreciation, Joel lifted Midnight. "You're welcome, Grandpa." Then he stared directly into his pet's eyes. "They're fluorescent!" remarked Joel.

"That's right," agreed Grandpa. "Midnight's more special than you thought."

"The whole night is. Thank you for helping me discover the dark, Grandpa. I kind of like it . . . when you're with me."

"So do I! This summer you and I will watch the fireflies turning their little lanterns on and off. But right now I'd better get back to the house, or Grandma will wonder where I am. Good night, Joel," he said as he turned homeward.

"Good night, Grandpa," returned Joel, and he headed toward his house. But as Midnight trailed him, he looked again to see the beacon light make one more revolution. "Midnight, maybe tomorrow evening we can spend more time discovering the dark." He scooped his cat into his arms and stroked her fur.

Midnight purred contentedly.

"And do you know what, Midnight?" asked Joel, although his cat could not understand. "God can see us in the dark just as well as in the daylight. Isn't that a cozy, comfy feeling?"

6

2. Giving Mother Away

Jane and Joe made a dash for the door. Julia didn't join in the race. She was struggling with her lunch bucket, her books, and the Mother's Day plant for Mother.

Of course seventh-grader Joe, with his long legs, won the race. But Jane wasn't far behind.

"What do you have there?" questioned Joe as Jane laid a gaily wrapped package on the kitchen table.

"My Mother's Day gift. It's nice Mother isn't home this afternoon when we're trying to smuggle her gifts into the house!" answered Jane.

"I'm glad too," added Julia. "I would never have gotten this flower in without her seeing it." She laid her second-grade library book on the table, then asked, "What is in your package, Jane?"

"A recipe book," answered Jane. "We each brought a recipe. Then the teacher compiled them into a book." Her sixth-grade teacher always had such clever ideas, and Jane knew Mother would be delighted with her gift. "What did you make, Joe? You didn't bring anything home for her, did you?"

Joe munched on his apple but answered between bites, "Brought it home the other day already."

"Brought what home?" wondered Julia. "What did you make?" She was a bit impatient with Joe's slow answer.

"Aw, you girls might tell. Better keep it my secret," teased Joe.

"Come on! Tell us!" demanded Jane. "It's no fair. You know what we're giving."

"Okay . . . promise you won't tell? Both of you? Positive?" Joe rolled his big brown eyes about as he challenged his impatient sisters.

"Don't waste our time," snapped Jane.

"And what makes you so busy?" challenged Joe.

"I have an idea for all of us," Jane replied. "We need every minute we've got until Mother and Daddy get home. So out with your secret, Joe. Then I'll tell mine."

Of course Julia was doubly curious now.

Joe wasn't quite sure about Jane's idea. Sometimes she came up with clever ones, but the next time they were good for girls only. "Okay, I'll say. I made a wren house in shop. Now, what's your bright idea all about?"

Jane spelled it out. "Today during study period I got to thinking. We're all making something for Mother. But what about dear old Grandma? There's a verse that says something about remembering your mother when she's old. Who'll remember Grandma if we don't? She's like our second mother because she's Mother's mother."

"Mother'll remember her. Always does for Mother's Day," replied Joe.

"That's right! And Mother is part of my gift idea!" continued Jane.

"How's that?" wondered Julia.

Jane went on with her plan. "You see Grandma is the one who raised our wonderful mother for us. Now Grandma's often lonely since she's a widow. Wouldn't it be nice if we children would 'give' Mother back to Grandma for a day?"

"How would we ever do that? I'd miss her!" Julia said, half fearful she'd lose her mother for good.

"You see, we'll all pitch in and do Mother's Saturday chores. We can begin right now. Then tomorrow Mother can go and spend the day with Grandma. Giving Mother for the day would be our gift to Grandma. Mother would enjoy having the day off too." Jane looked at her brother and sister's faces for their approval of her plan.

Julia agreed instantly.

Joe wasn't about to be caught up in what he considered women's work that easily. "Sounds okay for you girls," he admitted. "But I better go get the chores done Daddy told me to do when I get home."

After they all had changed clothes, the girls got busy and Joe headed for the barn.

The girls began by vacuuming and dusting the living

9

room. Next Julia took the old newspapers and tin cans out. She cleaned the washbowl and swept the kitchen floor.

Jane, a bit disappointed that Joe hadn't enthusiastically cooperated with her plan, was cleaning the windows. "If he doesn't help, I guess we girls can surprise her anyway," she concluded.

"What's that noise?" asked Julia. "There's someone on the porch."

"Look! There *is* someone on the porch!" answered Jane. "It's Joe! He's scrubbing the front porch. So he decided to help us after all. Great!"

In short order the furniture was dusted, the rugs were shaken, and the floor was washed.

"Can you believe we're almost done? Cleaning never goes this fast other times. And I didn't do a shipshod job either," stated Julia.

Jane giggled. "You mean *slip*shod." She was amused at her younger sister's effort to use new words. "No, we did do a good job of the cleaning even though we did it in a hurry. Guess that would be another gift for Mother, if we'd *always* hurry to get our chores done instead of making her coax us to work."

"Here are some bluebells I picked," said Joe as he entered the kitchen. "Got enough for a bouquet for Mother and Grandma. Then I picked a bunch of tea while I was in the meadow. I know Grandma likes tea."

"Oh, good! Thanks for helping us with the plan, Joe," said Jane, as she arranged the bluebells in a vase.

"Here they come! Mother and Daddy are here," called Julia.

The door opened. "Surprise!" chorused the three children. Then they told Mother they were "giving" her to Grandma for a day.

Joe, Jane, and Julia weren't disappointed to see Mother wipe tears from her eyes. They knew they were happy tears—the kind mothers cry when children honor their parents and grandparents the way the Bible teaches.

3. Peter, the Second

Eight-year-old Peter listened. *Is that Mother calling?*
Is she ready to go to Kessler's? Oh, I wonder if I'll be
allowed to go along.

Yes! There it was again. "Peter," called the voice that

was decidedly Mother's.

"Coming," Peter answered. He tilted the sprinkling can further to hasten the water to the last dry corner of the newly sown lettuce patch. There, he was done!

His sneakers sped across the freshly tilled soil in the direction of the patio.

There, at the picnic table, Mother was checking her seed inventory.

"Finished?" asked Mother.

Peter nodded, then gave her a quizzical look that asked, "What do you want?"

"Want to go along to Kessler's? You were speedy in getting chores done, so you may go along. Matthew's going too," said Mother.

"Yes! I do want to!" Peter replied. "As soon as I put the sprinkling can away, I'll get ready." Then he raced to the utility shed and hung the sprinkling can on its hook above the mower.

Meanwhile, Mother glanced up from her seed packets. She watched Peter dart to the shed, then into the house. "I'm surprised he remembered to put that away," she said mentally. "But that's Peter, a carbon copy of his daddy! His daddy's a good worker, organized, and interested in detail. Will he be a shop foreman too?" she wondered.

Now Mother's thoughts went back to the time Peter was learning to talk. *I won't forget his first sentence. He was playing with a few nuts and bolts, and as he managed to turn a nut on a bolt, he said, 'It fits.' He amused us all.*

Meanwhile, as Peter and Matthew were changing clothes, they were discussing their pleasure in going along to Kessler's. "Easter vacation is great!" declared Matthew. "We get to go along to Kessler's, my favorite store. Think we'll be allowed to go over to the toy department while Mother's getting her plants and seeds?"

"I hope so," Peter answered. "Even if we can't buy some new toys, I like to see what they have."

Soon the boys were dressed in clean clothes, combed, and seated in the minivan.

Mother checked her list and added one more item she'd forgotten. She headed for the garage. The boys were chattering happily as Mother climbed in and drove the five miles to the store.

When they arrived, Peter inquired, "Mother, may we please go over to the toy department while you get your things?"

Mother looked from Peter to Matthew and back to Peter. She knew how bored the boys would be while she was deciding on seed varieties and flower plants. "Okay. I guess you may. But remember the 'No Touching Rule.'"

Delighted, the boys headed to the shelves laden with tractors and equipment. There were also furry animals, chain saws that whirred like real ones, and stacks of table games.

Peter and Matthew became engrossed in wishful thinking as they surveyed the merchandise in each aisle.

"See this toaster," said Peter. "It actually pops up the toy bread slices like a real one. I wonder how it works." He reached for the sample toaster that was out of its display package.

"Peter, don't! Remember what Mother said," warned Matthew. "And see that sign!"

"Which sign?" asked Peter.

"There," said Matthew as he pointed to a neat little sign that stated:

Lovely to look at,
Wonderful to hold;
But if you should break it,
It's already sold.

"Oh, I forgot," said Peter as he quickly withdrew his hand. His eyes scanned the rest of the items in the aisle, while Matthew examined the baseball gloves.

Peter checked the end display of kites then sauntered up the Tonka toy aisle.

There they were! The bright red fire engines Peter had seen in the catalog were sitting waiting to be bought by eager boys.

"This one is different from the others," noted Peter. "You can extend the ladder. I wonder how it works." He reached for the little crank on the side.

The engine slid about on the metal shelf, so Peter had to use both hands.

The crank wouldn't turn.

He lifted it from the shelf to get a better grip. He tried to turn it. "What's wrong with this?" he wondered.

But, the ladder wouldn't budge.

Once more Peter yanked. Back and forth. "There it goes," murmured Peter. "I got it! I just need to wiggle it back and forth so it works more easily. Probably a squirt of oil would help." Peter kept turning the stubborn little crank.

Slowly but surely the ladder went up, up, up, until at last it was fully extended.

Peter smiled with satisfaction. He had gotten the crank to work. He turned to set it on the shelf. "Oh, it doesn't fit on there with the ladder up. I'll have to turn it down again," he noted.

The crank was even more stubborn now.

Peter tried to turn it backwards. He wiggled, coaxed, yanked, and finally forced it.

The ladder jerked downward. Again it jerked.

Peter persisted. He checked. "It almost fits. Just about a half inch yet and I can set it back," he estimated.

But the crank could not be persuaded. It would budge no further.

Peter put all the pressure on that his fingers could apply.

Crack! The crank snapped off.

Momentarily, Peter panicked, but thought quickly enough to bend the ladder just enough to jam the engine onto the shelf. He stuffed the crank into his pocket; then glanced up and down the aisle to see if anyone had witnessed his accident.

Matthew was coming. "Peter! Did you break it?" asked Matthew, with evident concern.

"No!" answered Peter quickly, as his cheeks turned crimson red.

"May I help you?" asked a sales clerk that seemed to appear from nowhere.

"Ah . . . a . . . no," Peter stammered.

"I thought I heard something snap," said the clerk. "You didn't break anything, did you?"

"No," Peter lied, while a knot in his throat seemed to choke him.

"Good. I always hate to make children pay for things they break," said the clerk as she turned to leave.

"Is there a problem?" asked Mother, joining the boys just then.

"No, there's no problem. I just thought I heard something break over here, but everything seems okay," said the clerk. Then she smiled at Peter and went to assist another customer.

"Did you break something?" asked Mother as she turned to the boys.

"No," answered Matthew.

"A . . . no," answered Peter.

"I'm glad," said Mother, "because you know you weren't supposed to touch anything. Now let's be on our way." She led the way to the exit door.

Peter felt horrible. He had disobeyed. He had lied three times.

It had all happened so quickly.

Peter shivered; yet his hands were hot and sweaty. Inside he was tied in knots—in his stomach, in his throat, and even in his head. Tears were ready to spill over, but he kept them in check. Like a mechanical toy, Peter followed Mother and Matthew across the parking lot.

Mother loaded her purchases into the van, fished the keys from her purse, and put the key into the ignition.

What shall I do? Tell or not tell? Oh, how horrible I feel! thought Peter. He hoped somehow the engine would stall to allow him more time to think.

Promptly the engine started.

"Wait! Don't go," called Peter.

"Why?" questioned Mother as she glanced into her rearview mirror.

Then the pent-up tears spilled over. "I did break a fire engine," Peter blurted out. "I didn't mean to. It just happened. The crank didn't work and I was trying to fix it."

Mother listened quietly.

More tears and sobs came. "And I told the clerk I didn't. And Matthew. And you," he added.

Gently, but firmly, Mother said, "Come, Peter. We're going back into the store. You will admit the lie and pay for the fire engine."

"But Mother, there was something wrong with the

crank. It wouldn't have broken if it would have worked okay."

"Would it have broken if you would not have touched it?" Mother asked.

Peter hung his head. "No, it wouldn't have," he admitted. "But Mother, one more thing. Can't we just buy the engine and not make a big fuss about it to the clerk?"

"Would that correct your lie to her? I'm sorry, Peter. You'll need to confess. Now come," Mother said, as she headed for the store entrance.

Peter knew she was right. *But how can I?* he wondered. His legs seemed too unsteady to carry him.

Too soon it seemed, they entered the toy department where the sales lady was stocking shelves. At least other customers were not around. She looked up and smiled, but when she noticed Peter, her smile was replaced by a somber expression.

"My son has something to say to you," said Mother. Then she placed her hand lightly on Peter's shoulder.

Somehow Mother's gesture helped give him courage to say, "I'm sorry I lied to you." A tear slid down his cheek. Then he added, "I did break a fire engine, and I'm here to pay for it."

The clerk took a deep sigh and said, "I'm glad you came back. After you were gone I happened to notice the crank was missing. I admire you for coming back." She smiled at Mother. Then she turned and said, "I'll get the engine for you and you can pay for it at the checkout."

When she handed the fire engine with the missing crank to Peter, he meekly said, "Thank you," and followed Mother to the checkout.

Once they had paid the cashier and the minivan was motoring home, silence reigned.

At home, both boys headed for the bedroom. Peter

sprawled across the bed and faced the wall. Meanwhile, Matthew changed into everyday clothes and headed for the door.

"Matthew," said Peter, "I'm sorry I lied to you."

"I'll forgive you," said Matthew and left the room.

Now Peter was alone and tears of regret and relief spilled out. How easy it had been to disobey! How hard to make things right!

A tap-tap-tap signaled that Mother was at the bedroom door. "Peter," she called softly, "do you care if I come in?"

"No," answered Peter.

She sat on the edge of the bed.

"I'm sorry, Mother. I disobeyed you and I lied to you. I didn't intend to do that. It happened so quickly," Peter finished.

"I'll forgive you, Peter. I'm rejoicing now. Not that you did wrong, but that you're sorry about your wrong," said Mother.

Peter sat up and reached for his bank on the dresser. He dumped its contents on the bed and said, "I want to pay you for the fire engine now." He counted the coins and dollars and handed them to Mother.

"Thank you," she said.

Peter noted that she looked sad, but relieved. It had been difficult for her too. But how grateful he was that she had helped him make things right.

A slight smile swept across Peter's face. "Mother, I just thought of Peter, the disciple. I lied three times, like he did. I could be called Peter the second."

"And remember, Peter," said Mother, "Jesus forgave Disciple Peter, and He'll forgive Peter the second too." Then she flashed him a heartwarming smile.

4. Different Mothers, Different Brothers

(Actual Persons)

John and Charles were brothers and they had sixteen more brothers and sisters. That's eighteen children in the Wesley family. Their father, who was a minister, was Samuel, and their mother's name was Susannah.

Do you suppose Mother Wesley was kept busy? I think so, because they lived in the country of England nearly three hundred years ago. Susannah couldn't go to the store and buy ready-made clothes for her children. She had to make their clothes. But before she could sew any clothes, she had to make the fabric by weaving cloth. First she needed to spin the thread, then weave it into cloth.

Even if the fabric would have been available, she couldn't have afforded to buy it, for the family was very poor. They had many debts to pay.

When Charles, their youngest, was eight years old they had a BIG disappointment and scare. Their house burned down! What a thing to happen to a family that was poor!

But do you think the Wesley family was unhappy? No. They enjoyed the time they spent together, especially the times they spent singing psalms together. Mother Wesley made sure she spent time alone with each of her eighteen children. She dearly loved them because she was a woman who loved and trusted God. She wanted to be sure her children would grow up to love God too.

Did they? Yes. John became a preacher, and he helped many people in England to learn to know Jesus. Later he sailed to America. There, in the state of Georgia, he taught others too.

Charles, the youngest brother, was busy helping his brother John with church work. The brothers always remained close in their boyhood and adulthood years. Even though Charles was busy, he found time to write songs. Six thousand five hundred of them! Four thousand were printed while he was living and the others were printed later. He wrote anytime, anywhere, and about any occasion.

You know the song "Jesus, Lover of My Soul," don't you? Charles wrote that. The Christmas song, "Hark! the Herald Angels Sing" and the Easter song, "Christ, the Lord, Is Risen Today" were written by him also.

When the boys were grown, Charles remembered his childhood and his mother. He said his mother was the one who helped him to learn to know God.

Now when we sing songs written by Charles Wesley we can be glad that Susannah Wesley believed in God and taught her children, even though they were poor.

* * * * *

Now let's "visit" another poor family who lived about seventy-five years after John and Charles Wesley died. Their home was located southeast of Blueball, Pennsylvania, in a wooded area called the Welsh Mountains.

Their home was very small—so small we would hardly believe that six boys, two girls, and their mother lived there.

The mother had become a widow when her second-to-youngest son, Isaac, was eight. She could hardly make ends meet. What could she feed them? Where would they be able to get something to eat?

Then the mother made a decision. She'd send her boys to the neighbors at night to get some eggs. Did she tell them to ask for some? No. She told the boys to steal them! What an awful thing to do! But since the boys weren't taught to love God, they found this egg-stealing to be quite exciting.

Soon stealing eggs was not sufficient. Why not steal chickens? The boys found this even more exciting.

Isaac said later, "I took to the crooked life as a fish to the water." That meant he enjoyed doing bad things his mother and brothers taught him to do.

When Isaac was twelve years old, he was sent to orphan's school. Here he was punished for doing wrong, but he disliked that greatly and ran away three times. The last time he ran away he headed back to his home area and worked for a farmer for three years. But Isaac didn't like to work.

So when Isaac was eighteen, he made up his mind he wanted to be a criminal. So did most of his brothers. (How good that two of the brothers, John and Martin, did learn to know Jesus later and became Christians.)

Isaac and his brothers, Abe and Joe, spent half of their lives in prison. They stole things and were put into jail. Then as soon as they were out of prison they stole some more. They even escaped from prison sometimes. Telling lies was common for them.

The brothers were smart, quick thinkers, but they used their God-given talent in the wrong way, the way their mother had taught them. It makes us sorry that this poor widow taught her sons how to steal instead of how to work and how to trust God to provide for their needs.

* * * * *

Now you've heard true stories of two different mothers who taught their sons different ways of living.

Each of us can ask, "Am I willing to follow the Christian example my mother is setting for me?" Secondly, "Am I thankful that I have a mother who tries to live a godly life herself and tries to teach me to do the same?"

23

5. M. S. . . . Guess Who

(M. S. — Actual Person)

Betty Brossman sank into the swivel rocker, her favorite chair. She rocked and swiveled, not knowing what to do with herself.

Brian, thirteen, who was five years older than Betty, was sprawled across the braided living room rug. His eyes were glued to the pages of *Hidden Rainbow*. Betty thought,

Wish he'd play a game with me instead of just reading.

Mother was rocking Baby Beth and reading softly to six-year-old Barbara Ann from *A Child's Garden of Verses*. Barbara Ann was rocking in her little rocking chair as she listened contentedly.

Meanwhile Daddy was stretched out on the sofa, relaxing. After a full day, he was glad for a leisurely evening at home.

Betty recalled the events of the day. *Good Friday . . . off from school. At church for services in the morning, at Uncle Fred's for dinner and at home tonight. Now what can I do this evening?* she wondered.

Just then Brian closed the book covers with a thud and announced, "Finished!" He rolled over on his back and stretched.

"Finished with your book already?" questioned Betty. "Will you play a game with me?"

"If the others help, I will," Brian promised.

"Daddy, will you help?" asked Betty.

"Depending on what you play," Daddy replied.

Next Betty solicited Mother and Barbara's participation. Mother promised to help as soon as Baby Beth was tucked into bed. Barbara Ann wondered what the game would be.

"I have a suggestion," said Mother. "Why don't we play a game our family played when I was a girl? I'll take Beth upstairs and when I come down I'll explain how to play."

"Do we need a card table or anything I can get ready while you put her to bed?" Betty asked.

"No. You won't need anything except your thinking caps," Mother answered as she ascended the steps.

The children tried to guess what game this could be. Mother soon returned and settled herself on the recliner.

"We called it guessing initials. Whoever is 'it' says someone's initials and the others guess who he's thinking of. 'It' may give clues to help them guess the correct person," Mother explained. "For example, I might say 'D. B.' Who would you guess that is? And I might add a clue like, 'He is a real historian and a wonderful father.'"

"D. B. . . . who could that be? Oh! I know. Daddy! David Brossman!" guessed Betty.

"Right," answered Mother. "Now you think of someone's initials and we'll guess."

The game turned out to be lots of fun. Some initials were easy to guess and others were difficult, requiring many clues.

Daddy came up with the most difficult one of all. "M. S. . . . guess who," he said.

"Milo Summers, our neighbor," guessed Brian.

"No. This person isn't living anymore. He lived about . . . let's see, about 450 years ago," Daddy concluded.

"Then it must be someone you read about in history," said Mother. "Give us more of a clue. We don't know history as well as you do, Daddy."

"I'm certain you've all heard of this man though, even if you don't know history well." Daddy started giving more clues. "He was born in West Friesland which is now the Netherlands. He came from a fairly wealthy family and his parents sent him to school instead of making him help to work to support the family like many boys needed to do at that time. Although he was Dutch, he could read and write Latin, and he knew some of the Greek language. So it appeared as if he would have an easy life. But many people hated him later in life because of a decision he made. In fact, they hated him so much they wanted to kill him. The Emperor promised a large reward to anyone who killed him, and their crime would be forgiven. Now can you guess?"

"Almost sounds like they hated him the way they hated Jesus and wanted to kill Him," Betty said, recalling the morning's Bible lesson. "The rulers offered money for Him too."

"That's right," agreed Mother.

Father added, "Yes, and this man believed on Jesus and believed the Bible was God's Word. Therefore he tried to live a true Christian life, although the church he grew up in didn't truly follow Jesus and His teachings. He became a priest in the Catholic Church when he was 28 years old, and he had a very easy life. He lived in sin, playing cards and drinking, but then he became curious about what the Bible had to say. He started to study it on his own, but he didn't tell anyone. Then after much reading, he became a Christian and was baptized."

"Must be an Anabaptist," Brian remarked. "Who baptized him if most of the people were Catholics?"

"A surgeon, barber, and elder named Obbe Philips. He was a peace-loving man and he baptized M. S.," answered Father. "Anyone have the answer?"

"What's an Anabaptist?" asked Barbara Ann.

"Anabaptists were people who believed they should not be baptized until after they became adults and could understand and believe what the Bible teaches. So if they had been baptized as infants, they were baptized again as adults. Understand?"

Barbara Ann nodded her head that she understood.

"I have an idea who it might be, but can you give us any more clues?" Mother commented. "You said they tried to kill him. Did they ever manage to?"

"No. He died of natural causes. God protected him although he was crippled in his later years and used a crutch. He was 66 when he died in Denmark. Because

27

he was crippled, he sometimes signed his letters: "Your brother, the cripple." That way the reader knew who wrote, but the authorities didn't know. His wife and son died before he did."

"So he had a family?" asked Betty.

"Yes. He had a wife named Gertrude, two daughters, and one son named John. His devoted wife was often sick and she faced many dangers with him. She was willing to be homeless to be with him. But one time she was sick and M.S. needed to keep traveling to get away from his would-be killers. She couldn't travel, due to her health, so she leased a house for herself and the three children. When the authorities discovered it, she fled and escaped. But they took the house away from the owners simply because they had shown kindness to Mrs. M.S.," Daddy explained.

"You say Mrs. M.S. One of these times you'll blurt out the name without thinking it," teased Brian.

Betty spoke next. "But I can't understand why the authorities didn't go into the churches where this man preached and get him if they wanted him so badly."

"They didn't have the blessing of buildings like we have," Daddy answered. "They worshiped in the dark, in the woods, in caves, wherever they could hide out. M.S. was known as the 'Night Preacher.' Even so, they had to be very secretive so news wouldn't get to the killers' ears. One time a traitor promised to capture him or he would lose his own head. The traitor tried his hardest to do this. He went to their meetings and spied out the places where they were assembled, but God helped M.S. escape. Later the traitor and an officer met M.S. in a small boat on a canal. Although the traitor knew M.S., he didn't tell the officer until the boat was close to the shore and M.S. had jumped to shore and escaped. The traitor then turned to the officer and said, 'See there, the bird has escaped us.' The officer became angry and called the traitor names because he hadn't spoken in time. The traitor replied, 'I could not speak, for my tongue was held!' The authorities severely punished the traitor. They didn't realize the same God M.S. feared, who shut the mouths of lions to protect the prophet Daniel, had also shut the traitor's mouth."

"Were M.S.'s friends also in danger?" asked Brian.

"Oh, yes! Anyone who took him into his home, gave him food or shelter, talked with him or had any of the books he wrote, was put to death. One man, Tjard Reynders, was baptized by M.S. and hid M.S. in his home. For this, Reynders lost his life."

"Those Christians were certainly tried for their faith," Mother said seriously. "We have it so good today." Then she continued with a twinkle in her eye, "And might the Mennonite Church possibly be named after M.S.?"

Daddy smiled. "Why, yes. It happens to be named after him, although he didn't like the idea because he wanted the believer's faith to be founded upon the Word of God, not on himself."

"Oh, I know," chorused Betty and Brian. "Menno Simons!"

"That's right," answered Daddy as he hopped up from the sofa. "You guessed it. But now, can any of you guess what time it is?"

"No, I can't," replied Mother. "But I do know it must be time for the three B.B.'s to get to bed."

"B.B.'s", who are they?" asked Barbara Ann.

"Brian, Betty, and Barbara Ann Brossman," said Mother.

The three children giggled, then bounded for the stair steps. "Good-night," they chorused.

6. Wooly Pants and Wilted Plants

"Hey, Walter, what's your last name?" asked Kevin as he winked at the other boys who formed an uncomfortable circle around Walter.

Walter hung his head, then meekly answered, "Weaver."

"Oh, my mistake. I thought you were Walter *Patches*," Kevin stated in mock seriousness. "Don't know where I got that idea. Always thought you were Walter Patches." He glanced obviously at Walter's patched pants and cleared his throat.

Snickers rippled from the other seventh-grade boys.

Walter's shoulders drooped and his worn sneaker scraped at the loose stones on the school driveway. He blinked back tears and slipped his hands into his pockets. His eyes glanced down over his knit pants, worn wooly from use. The patches on both knees seemed to be growing larger and more awkward by the second.

This was the worst episode yet with Kevin and the boys. Other times they mimicked in a singsong tone, "Walter Patches, Wooly Pants; Walter Patches, Wooly Pants," when he was up to bat. He could more easily ignore them during a game, but now . . . he couldn't pretend he didn't hear, because he was completely encircled. Self-pity sprang up inside Walter. "Sometime I'll get even with them," he promised himself.

The morning buzzer halted further words. The boys entered the classroom, settled into their seats, and passed knowing smiles to each other.

Walter pretended not to notice their glances as Mr. Witmer proceeded with the devotional period. Inside, Walter's hurt continued to brew into greater and greater self-pity and more and more revengeful thoughts.

"I'll be reading from the twenty-third chapter of Luke, concerning Christ's crucifixion," Mr. Witmer was saying.

Hope Kevin and the others get a sermon about being mockers, seethed Walter. *They deserve to have the Easter story preached to them.* Walter's thoughts continued to rehearse the morning incident over and over again. *It's not my fault. I can't help we're not rich. I don't like to wear patched, wooly hand-me-downs.*

Then something Mr. Witmer was saying goaded Walter's thoughts, bringing him back to the present. "Therefore, if we are wrongly accused or mocked it is important for us to have a Christlike attitude and pray on behalf of our adversaries. 'Father, forgive them, for they know not what they do,' was Jesus' way of responding. So it's not only our actions that are important, but our reactions as well. We need a forgiving spirit at all times. Now, let us pray."

The classroom was quiet as Mr. Witmer prayed. Walter's hands were clammy cold and beads of sweat covered his forehead, but his heart cried out to the loving Father who understood his longings and hurt. "Father, forgive me for the hatred I've felt toward Kevin and the others. I've been revengeful and unforgiving. With Your help I'll strive to react in a Christlike way from now on. And dear Jesus, may Kevin and the other boys learn to know You personally. In Jesus' name. Amen."

What peace! What calm! Walter felt a heavy burden lifted. Had the others had a change of heart? He hoped so.

But when recess time came, Walter was disappointed. The meaningful devotional period appeared to have been meaningless to his classmates. While the other boys continued to mock at every opportunity, Walter continued to utter the silent request, "God, help me control my reactions, in spite of their actions."

When school was dismissed, Walter biked home determined to unburden his troubles to Mother. He found her trimming at the flower bed. He related the morning's mockery, the previous incidents, his own hate, and the relief of having part of his burden lifted.

Mother listened quietly, then asked a few questions to be sure Walter was free from the mocking habit himself.

When she was assured of her son's innocence, she remarked, "Walter, you and your wooly pants are like those tomato plants." She pointed to a tray on the sunny porch. It held peat pots filled with spindly plants, withered and bent over.

"What do you mean? They're wilted plants!" he responded, a bit aggravated by her comparison.

"You see," she explained, "I planted the seeds indoors. How I rejoiced to see their first green blades come through. Then these seedlings began growing rapidly indoors. They became spindly and the stalk was weak. They could never withstand the wind and the sun if transplanted to the garden."

Walter listened intently, still not certain how he was like those wilted plants.

Mother continued, "Now I don't water them as often anymore, and I let the sun beat down on them. They wilt and look hopeless, but all the while their roots go deeper in search of water, and their stems become much thicker and sturdier when they are watered again. They'll be able to withstand more later in the garden because they've been tested as a seedling. They're just like a young boy. You need testing too, so you can withstand winds of temptation you may face someday. God knows if you learn to have a forgiving spirit now, you'll be stronger and more rooted when you're transplanted into adulthood. When you're grown, you may face even greater temptations to hold grudges, to be unforgiving, or to be revengeful."

"I get it," Walter said slowly. "If I'm laughed at now, I'll become stronger. But right now it's no fun to be mocked. I'll surely need God's help." Then he smiled, "I didn't know that by wearing my old wooly pants I would be like wilted tomato plants!"

7. Mrs. Antique Dealer

Wayne jingled the coins in his pocket. They were all his—the Kennedy half, the two quarters, the two dimes, and the one nickel. And he could spend them for whatever he pleased. Grandpa Wissler had said so.

Wonder if the other cousins all got the same amount,

he thought as his eyes scanned the crowd in search of his cousins, Dale and Ernie Wissler. *This is going to be a terrifically great day. First of all, I'm allowed to miss school to attend Great-Grandpa Wissler's sale. I never did that before—miss school when I'm not sick. Being with my cousins, buying lunch at the refreshment stand, and now Grandpa gave me money of my own to spend. That all stacks up to being a great—* Abruptly those thoughts were interrupted when he spied Dale and Ernie on the outskirts of the auction crowd.

Momentarily Ernie spied Wayne and nudged Dale to head in Wayne's direction. They slipped away from the crowd and joined Wayne.

Just then, Dick Clark the auctioneer struck his gavel on the auctioneer's rostrum. "Ladies and gentlemen, we're about to begin the sale of a fine lot of goods. I'm certain you've already noticed the good quality of this merchandise. We have antiques as well as newer items, and everything is in tip-top condition. Due to our blustery March weather we'll be altering the order of the sale somewhat."

He adjusted his microphone, then continued. "First, we'll be selling a few household items and old pottery, after which we'll move to the front yard and sell the furniture and appliances. If you haven't had opportunity to see what's out there yet, do so now. In half an hour, at 10:30, we'll be selling everything in the front yard from the 200-year-old chest to the year-old washer. We're asking each of the bidders to please make their bidding obvious to us so we don't miss anyone. All sales are final. If you haven't gotten your buyer's number, see the clerk inside the garage on the west side of the house. Let us begin."

Then Grandpa Wissler and some other men handed a

tray of cups and saucers to Mr. Clark. The auctioneer's voice rose and the bidding began. Some folks had the funniest ways of bidding. One man tipped his hat, another winked his eye, some fluttered their cards in the air to be sure they wouldn't be missed, while others simply nodded their heads.

"See how that lady over there twitches her nose when she bids?" questioned Ernie.

"Where?" wondered Wayne.

"Oh, yes, I see her," said Dale. "Look over there, Wayne. Behind your mother and dad. Those two ladies sitting on the lawn chairs. There now, they're talking together. The one's holding a cup and the other one is rubbing her finger over it."

"Oh, yes, now I see her. And she does have a funny nose to twitch," Wayne remarked.

"She can't help that though," reminded Ernie. "But look at all the jewelry she has on. She must be rich! All those dangling things on her wrist—and look on her ears too."

"The other one in the purple coat does too. See how they're rubbing their fingers over each of the cups and saucers. They hold them up toward the light and look into them. What are they doing?" Dale wondered.

"And did you hear how much she paid for them? Twenty-one dollars and seventy-five cents! Imagine! Paying that for Great-Grandpa Wissler's old everyday coffee cups. And if I remember right they had turned all brownish. I remember seeing them one time I was along when my mom stayed with them," Wayne recalled.

"Twenty-one dollars and seventy-five cents!" exclaimed Ernie. "I hadn't heard that. She wouldn't pay that much just to use them. They must be antiques. They're looking for cracks or chips."

"She's probably an antique dealer," Dale guessed. "Goes around to the sales and buys old things. Then she sells them in an antique shop or at a flea market."

"Flea market? You say *flea* market? What do you mean? A place they sell insects?" Wayne asked.

Dale and Ernie laughed at Wayne's puzzled look, then went on to explain. "A flea market is a swap meet where people come and have stands and sell their things. The things sold at a flea market are usually secondhand things or antiques. There's one close to our place."

Wayne laughed at his own mistake, then suggested, "Are you two hungry? Why don't we hunt up the refreshment stand?"

Agreed, the two boys and Wayne slipped out through the crowd, headed for the lunch wagon, and bought candy bars. Meanwhile the auctioning and bidding continued at a rapid pace.

Later the three boys enjoyed a hearty lunch purchased with money their parents had given them for that purpose. But the $1.25 from Grandpa remained in each of their pockets.

"What are they selling now?" asked Wayne.

"Postcards, they said," Dale replied.

"Hey, let's get over there. I'd like some of them for my collection. That's something I could buy with Grandpa Wissler's money," said Wayne, as he moved toward the crowd.

"You need a number, though," Ernie reminded.

"I know. I'll be back. I'm going over to Mother and Dad so they can bid for me." With those words, Wayne slipped through the crowd. *Now how can I get past these two antique dealers and their pile of purchases?* he wondered.

Just then, the one lady got up. "Where are you heading, young man?" she asked crisply. "I'd like to get out here."

"I'd like to talk with my parents sitting in front of you, if you'll please excuse me," Wayne said politely.

"All right, I'll wait here until you've passed. But be careful about it. Don't crush any of my purchases." Then pointing to a button box perched precariously on top of a three-legged flower stand, she added, "My button—"

But before Mrs. Antique Dealer could finish, the button box and its contents lay strewn across the ground.

"I . . . I'm sorry, Madam, I didn't mean to—"

"And sorry you shall be," she cut in. "Get to picking up and don't put any soiled buttons back into that box!"

Humiliated and hurt, Wayne squatted on the ground and picked up button after button. He recalled as a younger child he had thoroughly enjoyed playing with Great-Grandma Wissler's button box. Now the last time he'd ever see them had turned into an episode like this. Tears of embarrassment tried to push their way through. His cheeks were hot. And he didn't know what the outcome of this whole thing would be. Clutching a handful of dirty buttons in his one hand, he arose and handed the box of buttons to the irate lady.

"Here are the soiled ones," he managed to say. He noticed her nose twitched more than ever.

"How many are there?" she questioned.

Silently Wayne counted. "Twelve."

"You've just purchased them. That will be a dollar and a quarter. Perhaps this will teach you a worthwhile lesson, young man."

Wayne nearly choked as he reached into his pocket for the money Grandpa Wissler had given him. On Mrs. Antique Dealer's outstretched hand he placed the Kennedy half, the two quarters, the two dimes and the one nickel. He thrust his hand back into his empty pocket. Then he walked away to join Ernie and Dale. He just couldn't face Mother and Dad in front of all those people. He was certain they had observed the whole thing, and he was afraid he wouldn't be able to hold back the tears.

"Did you get the postcards?" asked Dale. "I saw your dad bidding on them."

Wayne was relieved that Ernie started talking before he had a chance to reply to Dale's question. Apparently they had not seen his encounter with Mrs. Antique Dealer. And Wayne was not about to relive the experience by telling his cousins.

"Wayne," Dad's voice said behind him, "will you please help carry these things out to the car? Then I want to go in and pay for the things."

After saying good-bye to his cousins, Wayne gathered up a box into his arms and headed for the car. Daddy walked along silently carrying sale purchases. After depositing the things in the trunk, Daddy pulled out a pack of postcards and handed them to Wayne.

"Wayne, we bought these as a remembrance for you. We thought you'd like them for your collection."

"Thank you," Wayne managed to say in spite of the lump in his throat.

"But, Son, the purchase you made at this sale will be worth more to you than these postcards ever will be. In the sight of God you spent your money wisely."

"But I didn't buy anything," Wayne started.

"Yes, you did. You bought a clear conscience by giving that antique dealer what she asked. You handled that situation in a Christlike manner. That was probably the wisest purchase you have ever made."

8. The Rescued Fledgling

Chirp, chirp, chirp.

It sounded like a distressed bird. Neil listened intently. Was it coming from the basement?

Neil's feet scampered down the basement steps. Then he stood silently, pricking his ears to catch any chirping sound. Was it in the basement somewhere? It wasn't the usual tweet-tweet of contentment. This bird was desperate.

Following the direction of the distress call, Neil headed toward one of the cellar windows. He wasn't aware birds could make such an unusual sound. He dragged the gray bench over to the window, then stepped up on his tiptoes so he could look out. There in the window well was a sparrow.

It was huddled in a little ball. Its body was still covered with fuzzy hair, although it obviously had sprouted a few new feathers on its wings and tail.

A feeling of sympathy welled up inside Neil. He needed to rescue this fledgling sparrow.

He noticed, however, that the little sparrow made not a squeak of noise. Where was all the chirping coming from? A close look showed two full-grown sparrows hopping about frantically, close to the edge of the window well. They hopped about from one ivy vine to another. They fluttered into the air, flew about, landed close to the window and looked down at the tiny bird. Their chirping continued at a stressful pitch. They were desperate.

Neil stood back far enough so they would not see him. *What's causing those two sparrows to act like this?* Neil wondered.

One of the grown sparrows flew away, wasn't gone long, then dropped seeds down the three-foot drop into the window well.

The baby bird hopped toward the seeds, and within a moment had gulped some down.

"That's the parents!" exclaimed Neil, aloud. "Their little bird probably tried to fly for the first time. It left the nest on its own, then fell into this window pit. The parents are all worked up because their little one can't get out. The male bird is providing food by dropping seeds so the little one can survive until it's rescued. I must call Daddy so he can open the window and rescue the little bird."

For about fifteen minutes Neil and Daddy watched nature's act through the basement window. Then Daddy opened the window, reached out, and cradled the tiny bird in his big hand. He handed it to Neil, then closed the window tightly.

"Oh, you poor thing! Your wings aren't strong enough yet, and you would have died if you wouldn't have had such a concerned mama and daddy. Aren't you awfully glad they care that much about you?" Neil asked the furry little ball. "Your parents were awfully upset when you got yourself into trouble."

Daddy's strong hand rested on Neil's shoulders. "Yes, those sparrow parents were awfully concerned about their little one. God gave special knowledge to birds and animals to care for young. But He has given human parents an even greater concern and responsibility for their offspring. Humans have not only a body to care for like this bird, but human parents have the additional care of their children's spiritual safety."

Neil looked up into Daddy's blue eyes, then glanced down at the rescued bird once more.

Daddy continued. "Now, that you're becoming a young man, you're somewhat like a fledgling. You are trying your own 'wings' more and more. But never forget, Son, our concern goes with you wherever you may 'fly.' God has given your mother and me this fear for your safety, both physically and spiritually. Don't be angry with us when we 'chirp' our concerns or corrections to you. Our prayers, love, and fear for your safety will follow you long after you've left our nest."

9. Borrowed or Stolen?

Eleven-year-old Keith Martin's blue eyes danced with delight as he sat on Grandpa's back doorstep. His cheeks dimpled and his lips broke into a smile, in spite of the fact that he was by himself.

It was normal to be by himself and to stay at Grandpa's on Saturdays while his parents needed to go away on church work. Normally he was kept busy running errands for Grandma, doing odd jobs for Grandpa, or helping dear old Mrs. Latshaw, the kindly widow who lived next door. Just last week he had carried her old newspapers out to her shop. Then he had sorted boxes of trash for recycling.

Therefore, sitting on the steps all morning was very uncommon. This morning he had offered to help if there was anything to do; but instead of giving him a job, Grandpa had given him a battery-operated car they had gotten for their grandchildren to play with.

The car was exactly like the one Keith had admired in the department store's advertisement. Its remote control switch could make it back up, turn around, drive straight, or go in circles. It even had headlights!

Just now Keith had maneuvered the model to stay on the walk all the way to the driveway. Skillfully he navigated a U-turn and the car sped toward the house.

The more he practiced, the better he could do it. So now his face reflected his delight when the model coasted right to his feet.

Just then Grandma called, "Keith. Dinnertime!"

"Already?" wondered Keith as he laid down the control and headed to the kitchen.

The aroma of apple dumplings filled the air. "Mmmm! It smells delicious, Grandma!"

Grandma chuckled, then challenged him, "Would you rather eat or keep playing?"

"That's a hard choice. Eating your apple dumplings or playing with the model are both superspecial, Grandma!"

Momentarily the three were seated around the table, bowing their heads in thanksgiving to God for His gift of food. Then they enjoyed the meat loaf, asparagus, and lettuce salad, followed by the warm apples rolled in

44

flaky crust and smothered with caramel syrup.

Keith enjoyed every bit of Grandma's meal, but as soon as it was over, he felt like rushing out the back door to resume his morning activity.

Christian courtesy, however, told him to do two other things instead. First, he thanked Grandma for her delicious dinner, and second, he helped clear the table and do the dishes.

When the last dishes were being stacked in the cupboard, Grandpa looked across the top of the newspaper he had been reading. "Keith, do you want to go along when I go to Overly's to get some saw blades sharpened? I have several other stops too."

Keith hesitated. "Do you mind if I stay here instead? I'd like to go, but I'd like to stay too."

Grandpa smiled. "I don't mind. I understand. You may as well enjoy yourself with the car until your parents get here." Then he headed to the garage. "Good-bye," he said to Grandma and Keith.

After Grandma's farewell to Grandpa, she said, "Keith, I'm going to be upstairs sorting through some things in our old chest. Call me if you need me."

"Okay," answered Keith as he headed for the back door. Soon he was holding the battery-powered switch again. He positioned the car to head down the walk, turned on the headlights, and then flipped the remote button to forward.

The car took off, but not as speedily as before. The farther it went, the slower it went till eventually it stalled completely.

What was wrong?

Keith wiggled the switch. He shook it and then tapped it against the palm of his hand. He looked for loose wires but found none.

Next he inspected the car. Nothing seemed amiss there. He flipped the switch again. The car remained motionless.

Dead, thought Keith. *The batteries are dead. I was running it all morning. Oh—I forgot to turn off the switch.*

He turned the battery case upside down and flipped out the battery cells.

Size AA, he observed. *Now where can I get replacements? I don't want to bother Grandma.*

An idea sparked in Keith's memory. Size AA—wasn't that the size he had seen last week on Mrs. Latshaw's shop table? He'd go check what size they were just in case they'd fit.

She probably wouldn't miss them anyway. Perhaps she'd forgotten she had them, he reasoned. He glanced to the Latshaw house. All was quiet. Mrs. Latshaw was probably taking her early afternoon snooze.

The commandment, "Thou shalt not steal" flashed through his mind.

Would that actually be stealing? he questioned. Of course he didn't want to steal! Stealing or borrowing, which was it? He didn't dare to answer himself honestly.

But if he didn't find batteries, he'd be left all afternoon without the car.

I'll just check what size they are, he decided. *That wouldn't be stealing.*

Glancing toward both houses, he made a dash across Grandpa's lawn to Mrs. Latshaw's shop. Then as quietly as possible, Keith opened the creaky shop door.

"Shh, you rusty hinges," he mumbled.

Keith stepped inside.

The shop, adorned with many cobwebs, was usually a fascinating place for Keith to explore. It was telltale of

46

Mr. Latshaw's hobbies prior to his death. Tools were scattered about among sawdusty patterns. Here and there stood half-finished projects. Shelves holding stain and varnish cans were above the workbench.

But Keith paid no attention to those things he normally liked to rummage through.

Brr. It was cold. Goose bumps danced up and down his spine.

He felt so . . . so . . . edgy for some reason. What was that? Did he hear someone?

He looked through the dirty, cracked windowpane that faced the house. No one was in view. Why did he feel so jumpy? He was just checking battery sizes, wasn't he?

He headed to the shop table. There they were. The new package of batteries. Size AA. The right size.

In a snap he swooped them up, jammed them into his pocket and dashed to the creaky door. He took a quick look toward both houses then darted across the lawn. Immediately he stuck the old batteries into his other pants pocket, tore open the battery pack, and inserted the new cells into the car. He turned it on.

The car whizzed right off the walk into the yard. It worked excellently! So it wasn't broken. It needed those batteries. Great! It was ready to run.

As Keith set the car back on the walk, he noticed the empty battery packet. Immediately he crushed the packet flat and stuffed it into his jacket pocket. No use raising any questions with that wrapper. He'd dispose of the trash at home somewhere.

He positioned himself on the step and turned on the switch. But this time the moving car was not as intriguing as before, nor was he as skillful in controlling it. Concentration was difficult.

47

The car zig-zagged this way and that. Next it upset.

As he was turning it right side up, a familiar voice startled him.

"Hello, Keith," said Mrs. Latshaw. "What an amusing toy you have there! I was going to ask a favor of you. But I don't want to interrupt you."

"Oh, oh . . . why, no, yes . . . I mean . . . What would you like?" stammered Keith.

"Would you climb a ladder for me? My legs are too wobbly to crawl up. I'd like the batteries replaced in my kitchen clock. It stopped running and I believe the batteries are dead."

Keith was only partially comprehending what else she was saying.

"I got batteries last week," she continued. "I thought I'd get you to replace them for me sometime when you're here. I meant to ask you last week when you took my papers out, but I forgot."

Keith rose to his feet. *What should I do next?* he wondered.

"I hate to spoil your fun here. But if you don't mind, it should only take a few minutes. If you'll get the ladder, I'll get the batteries. They're both in the shop," she said sweetly as she started toward the shop.

Keith was glued to the spot. What an awful predicament to be in. What should he do?

Mrs. Latshaw's steps halted. She turned to see why Keith, normally such a willing helper, would be reluctant to give her a helping hand.

What do I do? wondered Keith. *Tell her I borrowed those batteries? But no, when we borrow something we ask to use it and plan to return it. But I hid the battery wrapper. Are they borrowed or stolen?*

Mrs. Latshaw's wrinkled brow topped with silvery

white hair creased into a quizzical look. "Would you rather not?" she asked kindly.

Instantly Keith ran to her side, and he clasped her hands in his. His brilliant blue eyes looked into her faded blue ones and said, "Mrs. Latshaw, I'm so sorry!"

Tears spilled over and slid down both his cheeks as he explained. "I took your batteries. I told myself I'm borrowing them to use in that toy car. But really I wasn't borrowing. I stole them and thought you'd never miss them. I'm so sorry! I really am!" Then he dropped his head and released the handclasp. The tears became sobs of remorse.

Now the faded blue eyes filled with tears too. The aged wrinkled hands reached out and held the smooth young hands. Then quietly she said, "Keith, I forgive you. And I'm sure God will do the same. I want you to know that when a person gets to be my age, they have a lot of time to think and pray." She cleared her throat, then continued, "Keith, I love you and often pray that you will grow up to be a strong and honest man that God can use. I have high hopes for you."

A fresh flood of tears came from Keith's eyes.

Finally, he lifted his eyes to meet hers. "I will ask God to forgive me, and I promise you that with God's help I will never steal again! And I love you too, Mrs. Latshaw. Thank you for forgiving me. And do continue to pray for me. Now I'll go get the batteries out of the car, and I'll fix your clock."

10. Foolishly Fancy

"What's this?" asked Grandma as she saw the long, white envelope with the other mail. "Oh, it's not for us. It's for Wolgemuths. I wouldn't be getting a bill from Tracy's Department Store in New York City anyway!"

"Shall I take it over?" volunteered Kathy who was

spending several days at Granddad's. She was just too glad to have the opportunity to go to the mansion. The Wolgemuths had only one child—Wendy. She was nine, the same as Kathy.

"Yes, please do," replied Grandma. "But remember, in an hour we have lunch," she added with a smile. She knew the girls enjoyed each other's company in spite of their many differences.

"I'll be back in time," Kathy promised. "I don't want to miss out on your cherry pie!" With these words she sped out the doorway toward the Wolgemuths' house. She raced up the hill to the iron gate and pulled at the latch. The heavy gate creaked as it opened to a curving stone walkway.

Kathy listened for footsteps after she had rung the doorbell. Lucy, the maid, appeared all freshly starched, prim, and pretty.

"Good morning. May I help you?" greeted Lucy. Her manner was formal, but pleasant.

"Yes. The mailman left this envelope in Grandma's mailbox. It's for the Wolgemuths."

"Very well. Please step inside. I'll call Mrs. Wolgemuth."

Kathy felt very small and strange as she waited in the foyer. As always, she was fascinated by the long, winding staircase.

"Good morning, Miss Mail Lady," greeted Mrs. Wolgemuth with a smile as she took the envelope. "May you stay to play with Wendy? She would be delighted."

"I may stay for forty-five minutes."

"Fine. Wendy is trying on her new Easter dress I purchased while my husband and I were in New York City. In fact this envelope you delivered contains the bill for it," she added. "Do you know where her room is?"

"Oh, yes."

"Then go on up and knock on her door. Tell her who you are, and she'll appear in a flash."

Kathy ascended the plush, carpeted stairway and rapped on the door. "Wendy," she called. "It's Kathy."

A shriek of delight sounded from within, and the door swung wide open.

"Kathy!"

"Wendy!"

Both girls were overjoyed to see each other.

"Wendy, what a lovely dress!" exclaimed Kathy as she admired the ruffled, mint-green dress. Each ruffled tier of the skirt was lace-edged. The darker green sash accented the waist and was tied in a big bow in the back. Kathy had never seen such a pretty dress . . . never!

"It's my Easter dress. I suppose you have one too," said Wendy.

"Well, —er—a—n–no, not really," stammered Kathy.

Wendy looked shocked. "No Easter dress? Aren't you going to church Sunday? It's Easter, you know."

"Yes, we always go to church," answered Kathy.

"Always? Did you say we? Your mother and dad too? Do they always go too?" Wendy chattered on. Her parents went to church only on Easter. Other times she rode the church bus that came by every Sunday morning. She asked more questions. Kathy's way of life seemed so different to her, so simple.

"But you will go to the beauty parlor before then, won't you?" she asked.

"Beauty parlor?" asked Kathy.

"Yes, to get your hair done," said Wendy.

"No, Mother will comb me as usual," answered Kathy. She was glad Wendy had said "to get your hair done," because Kathy wasn't sure what a beauty parlor was.

Wendy seemed to forget to ask more questions about Kathy's unusual Easter as she modeled her new, white, patent-leather shoes and her new, green hat with the long, white ribbon streaming down her back. Then the girls began chatting about other things, and the forty-five-minute stay soon ended.

On the way back to Grandma's, Kathy decided to ask either Mother or Grandma why people celebrate Easter so differently. She knew the answer—somewhat. It just didn't seem right to spend such an important day thinking about clothes. It seemed like God should have all the glory and praise for what He did. *I'd be busy thinking of myself instead of God if I wore that dress,* Kathy thought. *I wonder what the Bible says about dressing that way.*

Grandma was glad to answer Kathy's question. "The Bible certainly does have something to say about that," she began. "In speaking to Christian women, the Apostle Peter said, 'Whose adorning let it not be that outward adorning of plaiting the hair, and of wearing of gold, or of putting on of apparel; but let it be the hidden man of the heart, in that which is not corruptible, even the ornament of a meek and quiet spirit, which is in the sight of God of great price.' Makes fancy dressing seem pretty foolish, doesn't it?" added Grandma.

"Easter's the day to remember Jesus' death and resurrection and what they mean to me," Kathy decided. "I'm afraid a fancy dress would keep me from being pleasing to God."

11. Jonathan "Cures" Craig's Meanness

"Mother, what is this word: N-O-N-R-E-S-I-S-T-A-N-C-E?" spelled Jonathan. He was doing his homework at the kitchen table.

"That word is nonresistance," answered Mother as she continued to stitch on Marilyn's dress.

"What is nonresistance?" questioned Jonathan.

Mother snipped a thread, then looked at Jonathan. "Nonresistance means that a person does not fight back, but treats those kindly who are unkind to him. Remember how Jesus responded when He was crucified?"

Jonathan remembered because he had just heard the Easter sermon on Sunday. "Do you mean like when the soldiers took Jesus, Peter wanted to fight back and cut off someone's ear, but Jesus told him not to?"

"That's right," answered Mother. "He even healed the soldier's ear. Also while Jesus was nailed to the cross He prayed that God would forgive those who treated Him so cruelly."

After some time Jonathan shook his head. "That's terribly hard to do though!" He remembered the incident at last recess all too well.

At lunchtime Craig Kauffman had hurled a "spinner" ball and had hit Jonathan in the stomach. Jonathan felt certain that it hadn't been an accident. For the past several weeks the resentment between the two boys had seemed to keep growing. Now, this baseball hadn't only hurt Jonathan's stomach, but it had also hurt his pride. So at last recess Jonathan had determined to cure Craig of his meanness.

"Are you finished with your homework?" wondered Mother. "You seem to be daydreaming."

"Oh . . . a . . . yes . . . almost," answered Jonathan as his thoughts returned to the present.

"As soon as you are done, I have something to show you children," said Mother.

Jonathan finished in short order. Soon Jonathan, his sister Marilyn, and his brother Andrew were gathered about Mother. Jonathan squatted on the floor at Mother's feet.

On her lap Mother held a huge book. "This book is called the *Martyrs Mirror*. It is filled with true stories of people who were nonresistant. Because they were Christians, they didn't fight back."

"Read us some of the stories," begged Marilyn and Andrew.

"I shall tell you one of the stories. If I read them, you may not understand. Here is a story of Dirk Willems," continued Mother.

"Is that a picture of him?" Jonathan wondered as he pointed to a sketch of a man helping another man out of icy water.

"Yes, that's he," answered Mother. "Dirk Willems lived in the country of Holland. He was a Christian who had been baptized. Because the rulers of that city did not believe as Dirk did, they wanted to kill him. The burgomaster or mayor of the town told the thief-catcher to catch Dirk. Dirk ran across ice-covered waters. Although it was difficult, he made it safely to the other side. But when he got over, he saw that the thief-catcher, who had been chasing him, had broken through the ice. What do you suppose Dirk did then?" asked Mother.

"Quickly ran and hid," suggested Jonathan.

"That's probably what he felt like doing. But because he was a Christian, he wanted to be kind to his enemy. So he returned and helped the thief-catcher out of the water."

Wide-eyed, Andrew asked, "What happened to Dirk then?"

"He was caught," answered Mother. "The thief-catcher wanted to let him go because of his kindness, but the burgomaster would not allow it. Because of Dirk's kindness, he lost his own life."

"How awful!" exclaimed Jonathan.

"Yes, it is sad," agreed Mother. "But because Dirk followed God's commandments until he died, he could look forward to living in heaven. Being in heaven is so much better than being chased and hated on this earth."

Jonathan, Marilyn, and Andrew went to bed after hearing the story of Dirk. But Jonathan couldn't sleep.

If Dirk was kind to someone who wanted to kill him, why, oh, why, did I take revenge against someone who only hit me with a baseball? Then quietly he slipped out from under the covers and knelt beside his bed. "Dear Father, I'm sorry. Forgive me for purposely tripping Craig on the asphalt so that he scuffed his knee. I know it was hate instead of love that made me do it. Thank You for teaching me what nonresistance is. Help me to be nonresistant like Dirk Willems. Thank You for Jesus who taught us to love those who treat us unkindly. And help me to say I'm sorry to Craig tomorrow. In Jesus' name, I pray. Amen."

Jonathan was soon fast asleep.

12. King David, Anne Sullivan, and You

(Actual Persons)

King David and Mephibosheth

The Bible tells of a little boy called Mephibosheth who lived long, long ago. Mephibosheth's father was Jonathan, a good friend of King David.

One day when Mephibosheth was five years old

something bad happened to him. There was fighting and Mephibosheth's family had to flee. The nurse who was carrying Mephibosheth dropped him, and what do you think happened? He became lame. Lame in both his feet! Now he was a cripple.

What would happen to Mephibosheth? His father and his grandfather had died. Who would take care of him?

But one day he received word from King David. King David wanted to see him. Mephibosheth felt as if he weren't worth more than a dog in the sight of the King.

But because David wanted to do what was right in God's sight, he insisted that Mephibosheth should be given land and from then on he should eat at the king's table.

What joy David brought into the life of crippled Mephibosheth!

Anne Sullivan and Helen Keller

In the late 1800s in Tuscumbia, Alabama, a little girl was born to Arthur Kellers. They were happy to have this first child in their home. She was named Helen.

Helen's parents loved to see her grow and learn new things. The day Helen was a year old she learned to walk. But before she was two years old something terrible happened. Helen became very ill and the doctor did not expect her to live.

She didn't die, but the illness left an ugly scar on her life. She could no longer hear, but even worse, she had become blind. Poor little Helen would have to spend the rest of her life in silence and darkness. It seemed as though she were shut up in a black closet where no sound or light could get in.

Life was not pleasant for Helen. Neither was it pleasant for her parents because they could not talk to her and teach her. When the Kellers sat down at the table to eat, Helen would run around the table and grab food that smelled good off the other people's plates.

How could she be taught to sit and eat? Although her parents loved her, they were at a loss to know how to help her. They pitied her too much to make her obey.

Then baby Mildred was born into the Keller family. Blind Helen didn't know what the little thing was in the cradle. So she grabbed at it and tried to toss it to the floor. Mrs. Keller rescued the baby before it hit the floor, but now she and her husband knew Helen needed help desperately.

The help they found was a twenty-year-old woman named Anne Sullivan. This young lady came from Boston to the Keller home to be Helen's teacher. Helen was almost seven years old when Anne arrived.

Anne knew Helen needed to learn obedience before she could be taught anything else. At the breakfast table Helen made a dive at Anne's plate and grabbed a handful of scrambled eggs. Anne pushed her hand away. On the second try, Anne slapped Helen's hand. Helen didn't understand what this stranger in the house was doing to her, so she threw herself on the floor and kicked and screamed. But Anne was strong. She pulled Helen up, shook her, and set her firmly on her chair. Helen tried to bite her. The struggle continued for several hours. But finally Helen gave up, and Anne began to teach her how to eat with a spoon.

Anne knew the job of teaching Helen was going to be difficult, but she understood Helen. Anne herself had at one time been blind. Her own childhood had been very unhappy. Anne's mother had died when Anne was eight, and two years later her drunken father had deserted Anne and her crippled brother Jimmie.

Nobody wanted to take in a blind girl and a little crippled boy, so they were sent to a poorhouse at Tewksbury, Massachusetts. What an awful place this was! There were no other children there, and many of the people were old or senile. Anne and Jimmie clung together amidst terrible conditions, but Jimmie's health became worse and worse. Finally Jimmie died.

Four years later, when Anne was fourteen, she was sent to a school for blind children. She entered first grade because she had never attended a school before. The other children made fun of her. A year later a doctor operated on her eyes, and she was able to see to read and write. But all her life her eyes remained weak, and she wore darkened glasses. Knowing the struggles a blind person can face, Anne was determined to make Helen Keller's life as normal as possible.

Anne taught Helen to run, skip, and jump like other children. Stringing beads and crocheting yarn became delightful pastimes for Helen under her teacher's helpful supervision. Her teacher also spent much time forming letters with her fingertips in Helen's hand. Anne knew this would be the only way Helen could learn to talk to others.

Anne kept signing words into Helen's hand, but Helen didn't understand. She thought it was a game. One day at the pump trough Anne kept dipping Helen's hand into a cup of water and spelling W-A-T-E-R into her other hand.

Suddenly Helen caught on to the idea that W-A-T-E-R meant that cool something she was feeling. She became excited as she realized everything she could touch had a name. She ran about touching things and then returned to Anne to have her spell in her hand what it was. What an important day for Helen! It was the first time she had ever "talked" with anyone. This eventful day was exactly one month and two days after Anne had come to live in with the Kellers. As the years passed, Anne continued to help Helen learn new things. She accompanied her to school and read the books to Helen. When Helen went to college, Anne continued to be "eyes" for Helen, even though her own poor eyes ached from overuse.

Incredibly, Helen not only learned to write, but to speak. Many people became interested in her, and she became famous, although she was hardly aware of it.

In her adult years, Helen wrote books and spoke to crowds of people in order to support herself and Anne. But she was never rich because she was always trying to help other blind persons. How encouraged blind people were when they heard Helen speak to them! But Helen did not take credit to herself. She felt Anne Sullivan, her teacher, had made all the difference in her life.

You and I

Now that you have read of King David's kindness to a cripple and Anne Sullivan's kindness to a blind and deaf girl, you may wonder what you can do for others. Although we don't have riches to give like a king and we may not be able to give our whole life to help one person, we can still do good as we have opportunity. Jesus said if we do kindnesses to others, it's like doing them to Him. So even if we can't do big things, we can do little kindnesses for others. A little kindness can be a big encouragement.

13. Shortcut Priscilla

A Story From Long Ago

Priscilla stepped into the cabin doorway and across the sod floor. Her long auburn plaits thumped against her homespun dress. Priscilla had managed to comb herself this morning. In spite of her thick hair and the numerous tangles due to yesterday's washing, she had managed to get most of the strands into the braids. Her part wasn't straight. Neither was it exactly in the middle, but so what. Getting done was more important to her than getting things done exactly right.

Today Priscilla had no time to waste. She was hoping to get some free time later in the day. The willow basket she was working on required only about one more hour of weaving. How she would like to finish it!

If only she didn't have to work so hard and long. She seldom got to do the things she liked to do most. There was always work, work, work, ever since the Webers arrived in America.

"In Holland, I never had to work so hard. Nor so long," sighed Priscilla. "We get up long before the sun, and I can't relax on my chaff bag till long after the sun has sunk behind the woodshed. When will I get a chance to sit by the lamplight to read?" She longed to reread one of the family's three books.

Mother Weber was outside stirring the boiling lye and cracklings. Making soap was a tiresome job.

I'm so glad Priscilla is getting older, thought Mother Weber. *She seldom complains. I appreciate how she takes over in the house when I'm outside. Her last batch of bread was practically as high and fine-textured as mine. For an eleven-year-old she does quite well. That is, until she dreams up another shortcut. How can I teach her the importance of doing things the way she is told?*

Yesterday was a good example of Priscilla's shortcut habit. On the way to the herb garden for some catnip tea, Priscilla decided a shortcut would be in order. Instead of using the beaten path as she had been told, she decided it would be quicker to cut across and follow the rock ledge. Nathanael, who had just turned three, was beside her.

"Come, let's go this way, Nathanael," called Priscilla.

"No! Mama say not! Me go on path. No get poison ivy here," he answered stubbornly.

"Okay, go that way," Priscilla said crossly. "I'm taking a shortcut. I'll be back at the cabin before you even get to the garden." Priscilla turned and gave one last look. Nathanael wasn't following her so she was on her own. "Maybe I can pick some honeysuckles along the way," she decided.

The rock ledge was solid evidence of the long hours the family had spent picking up stones. After Father Weber had felled the trees and cleared the land for farming, the whole family had joined in the task of picking up the limestones.

Priscilla's bare feet nimbly hopped from one rock to another. Her calloused soles didn't mind the heat of the sun-warmed boulders and rocks.

Priscilla felt happy and free. Her whistled tune floated on the breeze.

"I'm glad I decided to take the shortcut," mused Priscilla. "A minute saved is a minute earned for basket—"

Her thoughts stopped short.

Sharp pain stabbed the sole of her right foot.

"Ow! Ow!" she wailed as she lifted her foot for a closer look. She had cut her foot on a jagged piece of broken stone jutting up from the rocks. Blood dripped to the ground, and pain shot through her foot.

"Ow! Ow! Ow!" Priscilla moaned as she tried to brush the dirt from the wound. Droplets of blood dotted the trail as she hobbled towards home.

What will Mother say? Now she'll know I didn't stay

on the path to the garden. But, I was only taking a short-cut . . . I didn't really mean to disobey.

Tears from the pain mixed with tears of regret and slid down Priscilla's suntanned cheeks. If only she hadn't tried that shortcut!

But what will Priscilla do when another shortcut idea pops into her head? Will she follow her own thinking or obey?

* * * * *

"Priscilla! Priscilla, time to get up," called Mother Weber.

Priscilla turned over on her chaff-bag bed and rubbed her eyes. Tiny streams of sunlight peeked through a crack between the logs where the chinking had fallen out. She pushed the patchwork coverlet aside.

"Coming, Mother," answered Priscilla. The smell of buckwheat cakes and frying sausages filled the room and invited her downstairs for breakfast. *That smells de-e-e-licious!* she thought as she patted her empty stomach.

Priscilla hopped to her feet. "Oh, ow! I forgot about my cut I got yesterday," she muttered aloud. "I guess that's what I get for taking shortcuts." She pulled on her clothes and limped downstairs to the kitchen.

Mother Weber greeted her daughter with her usual cheery good morning. Then she asked, "How's your foot this morning? Any better?"

"I guess it's better than yesterday, but it still hurts. I had forgotten about it until I stepped on it."

"Well, has my girl learned her lesson?" asked Father Weber. "How many shortcuts do you plan to take today?"

"None, Daddy. I hope I'll always remember to obey rather than take shortcuts."

Now the family gathered around the breakfast table.

They always bowed their heads and thanked God for their food. Pioneer families had too many fires, droughts, and other trouble to take the blessing of food for granted.

The chatter around the table centered around the day's duties. Priscilla's jobs for the morning were to do the breakfast dishes, bring a supply of water from the spring, and string the sugar peas for dinner.

Priscilla cleared the table. Next she dipped hot water from the kettle in the fireplace into her dishpan. "Now, where's the soap?" she wondered. Then she remembered the last little bit had been used for the supper dishes. *Ah, the breakfast dishes aren't that dirty. Why waste the time to run for soap?* she thought.

"Shortcut Priscilla! Shortcuts today again?" questioned a little voice inside her.

"No, I guess I better not. Mother wants hot, soapy dishwater used. No shortcuts today," she decided as she headed for the box of homemade bar soap.

The dishes were soon sparkling clean and put away in the cupboard. After the water containers were filled with spring water, Priscilla started with the sugar peas.

"Sugar peas are so good," sighed Priscilla. "They're the first thing we get from the garden in the spring. That makes them extra special. But I only wish it wouldn't take so long to do them."

Nathanael was outside making mud pies. Then he giggled as he chased a baby rabbit which hopped to the side of the cabin. He didn't have many chores. He could play all day because he was only three years old.

"It's not fair. Nathanael doesn't have to work," muttered Priscilla. No one was in the house to hear her, but she didn't care. She felt better if she complained, even if no one heard her.

Her one-sided conversation continued. "Only half done with the sugar peas! I won't get to finish weaving my basket today again. Why are sugar peas made with strings anyway? String beans are called string beans. The string beans we grow hardly have any strings since we've been saving seeds from the least stringy ones. We just snip the ends off string beans."

The more Priscilla thought about why sugar peas have strings, the slower her hands worked. The basket of peas didn't seem to get less.

Then the idea struck her. "If beans don't need stringing, sugar peas don't either. I'll just clip both ends off and no one will know. What a time-saver! I'll be done in short order." And that's how Priscilla finished the job.

Mother Weber entered the cabin just as Priscilla was putting her basket and knife away. "Done already?" Mother Weber questioned in surprise. "That's good. You must have kept your mind on your work and kept those fingers busy. Now, wash them and put them into the kettle. Then you're free until I need your help to set the table."

Priscilla ran to get her basket supplies. She took the willow and her unfinished basket outside to work on them. But too soon Mother's call came to set the table.

Shortly, the family gathered around the plank table. Everyone eyed the dish of sugar peas. How good they looked! After silent prayer, the deer roast, potatoes, and peas were passed.

"Oh! What the matter wif the peas?" asked Nathanael. "Me not like them!"

At the same time Father's mouth felt something was wrong too. "Some of them are all right, but others are stringy," he said.

A surprised look crossed Priscilla's face. She took a

spoonful and knew immediately what the problem was. Mother and Father both guessed what was wrong at the same time.

"Do you care to explain what's wrong with the peas, Priscilla?" asked Father.

Tears sliding down Priscilla's cheeks told the story. "I thought I had learned my lesson yesterday with my foot," she cried.

Now Father spoke, kindly but firmly. "Priscilla, habits are hard for everyone to break. But the older you get, the harder it becomes to stop. Do you really want to break the shortcut habit?"

"Yes," was Priscilla's weak but honest answer.

"Then you'll need to ask God to help you. Every time you're tempted to take a shortcut, ask God to give you the strength to say no. You've been doing this so often it's hard to stop. But God can change you into an obedient and dependable child," advised Father.

"I will. I'll always remember these stringy sugar peas," announced no-more-shortcuts Priscilla.

SUMMER

14. Does Anyone Understand?

Twelve-year-old Marlin was looking forward to the gathering of Daddy's family for the annual picnic.

"Mother," he'd ask each year toward the end of the school term, "isn't it soon time for the Newswanger picnic?"

"Yes," she'd answer. "It's always held the third Saturday of June, the day before Father's Day."

Marlin would smile and say, "I can hardly wait. I like my friends at school, but playing with my cousins is even better. You know Daddy and the other men always help us play games."

But this year things would be different. Two months before the picnic, life had changed drastically. What would the day be like?

It began as usual with everyone gathered around the smoking barbecue grills. The aroma of sizzling chicken filled the air.

Soon the womenfolk were busy as bees setting the tables. Marlin's mother did likewise, placing their two plates side by side, one for her and one for Marlin.

After lunch and lots of visiting, the uncles, aunts, and cousins all congregated at the ball diamond. While the teams were being picked, Marlin overheard a comment on the sidelines, "I believe everyone is here."

Marlin felt a stab of pain in his heart. *What do they mean everyone is here?* he questioned silently. *Don't they remember or understand? Everyone is not here!*

Just then Uncle Ralph called, "Marlin, ready to bat? Batter up! It's your turn."

Promptly Marlin dismissed his thoughts and grabbed the aluminum bat. After all, the ball game was the highlight of the picnic.

Marlin touched the bat against home plate. He tilted his cap until its bill shaded his eyes from the sun's glare. Now he was set. He'd give the game his best.

Cousin Jeffrey, the pitcher, hurled the ball toward the plate.

Marlin swung. Wham! As the ball whizzed past the outfielder's glove, Marlin raced to first. Then second. On to third.

71

At third he hesitated. *Can I make it home?*

"Go! Go! Go!" shouted his teammates. "You can make it! Make it a homer!"

He dashed towards home. Casting a sideways glance, Marlin spied the ball whirling toward the catcher. *I've got to slide to make it!*

He slid and his left foot touched the base.

"Safe!" the others shouted with glee. An exuberant round of cheers followed.

"Good hit!" complimented Uncle Ralph as he proceeded to take his turn at batting.

"Thanks!" Marlin managed in spite of the lump in his throat. His eyes remained glued on Uncle Ralph.

Ralph's features bore a striking resemblance to Marlin's father. The muscular arms and legs. And those smile lines radiating from Ralph's eyes were a definite family trait.

If only Uncle Ralph's brother were here, thought Marlin. *How different this picnic would be if everyone were here! Does anyone understand?*

Marlin's attention was again diverted to the activity on the ball field.

Uncle Ralph had tried to steal to third base and was caught between the second and third basemen. Like a boomerang, the ball flew back and forth from glove to glove. Now the second baseman caught it, but oh, he fumbled! The ball dropped and instantly Uncle Ralph was safe on third.

Cheers and groans ensued. Thus the ball game continued. Everyone was enjoying the family fun. Even Marlin had forgotten his problem for the moment. By now the score was twelve up, a tie!

Then Uncle Ralph glanced at his watch. "Do you know what time it is?" he asked in surprise. "It's four o'clock!"

Adults and children both knew four o'clock meant it was time to gather things together and head homeward.

Marlin grabbed his glove and bat and threw them into the car trunk. Next he helped Mother carry the ice chest to the car. Then he plopped into the passenger seat and patiently waited until Mother had said her good-byes.

Mother crawled in and drove down the gravel lane.

I'm sure glad I have her yet, he thought. *I'd be all alone without her.* Then Marlin began noting the complete families heading for their homes. As he watched, the old familiar lump was again growing in his throat. Would he choke or would tears spill out first?

Marlin glanced at Mother. She seemed unusually quiet too. Ever since the accident, life hadn't been the same.

As they traveled homeward, they passed a shopping mall on the outskirts of Staunton. The show window at the department store displayed a large banner: "Remember Father's Day. Buy your cards and gifts here."

"Wish I could!" he blurted out.

"Could what?" asked Mother, a bit concerned. It wasn't like Marlin to seem so upset.

"Forget it. I shouldn't have said it, Mother."

"Marlin, please tell me. I'll try to understand."

Marlin hesitated, but he could stifle his tears no longer. "The sign at that store said, 'Get your Father's Day card and gift here.' That hurt because I missed Daddy so much at mealtime, and then I made a home run and he wasn't there to be glad with me. Then when everyone left, each car held a complete family, except ours."

"I understand, Marlin. More than you may know.

Sometimes I question, 'God, why did that tractor trailer cross the center lane and snatch the life of my dear husband and Marlin's loving father?' But that isn't a good thing to ask. With God things don't just happen. He has our lives under His control." Marlin listened as Mother continued, "We certainly are more blessed than our neighbors, the Oswald family."

"What happened to their daddy? I know there are three children living with their mother."

"Their daddy wasn't a Christian," Mother explained, "and he no longer wanted to be the husband and father in their home, so he left them. Your daddy prayed for you and me, and God is still answering those prayers."

"Doesn't God take care of the Oswald children then?" wondered Marlin.

"He will if they ask Him," answered Mother. "He loves everyone. God has promised to be a Father to the fatherless. He has also promised to hear the prayers of the widows. That is such a comfort to me. He understands and cares."

"Mother, I don't fully understand what all you explained, but I do feel better. It's good to know God understands, even if others don't."

"This little talk helped me too, Marlin. Sometimes I also wonder if anyone understands, but perhaps other people understand and care for us more than we think they do. Everyone today wanted to know how we were doing, and I'm sure many friends are praying for us. When we feel sad and lonely, we can always talk to God. He understands us completely."

"There's just one thing yet, Mother. I dread tomorrow, being reminded of Father's Day."

As Mother flicked on the turn signal to make a right turn into their driveway, she said, "Marlin, between you and me, shall we make Father's Day a kind of Thanksgiving Day instead? Let's be thankful God gave you a Christian father who has left us many happy memories. And then, let's be especially thankful for our heavenly Father, who cares for us."

A faint smile played across Marlin's face as he gave Mother a nod.

By now Mother was stopped in front of the garage.

Marlin hopped out to open the garage door for her. That old familiar lump in his throat had almost disappeared. It helped to know that Someone does understand.

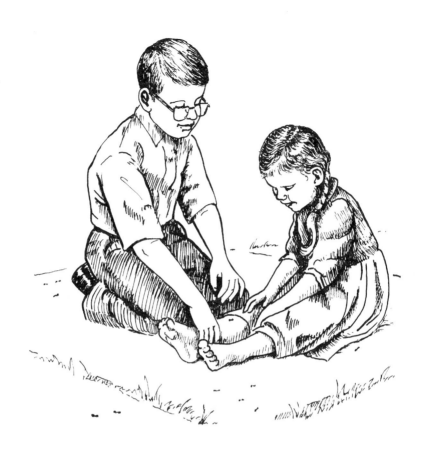

15. Considerin' an Ant

"John, what are you doing?" called four-year-old Amanda.

"Oh, I'm just considerin'," answered John as his eyes remained glued to the sidewalk.

"Considerin'? What do you mean?" asked Amanda, a bit vexed that John continued to give the sidewalk more attention than her.

"I'm considerin' an ant. That's what I'm doing," replied John.

Curiosity got the best of Amanda. She had to see what was taking John's attention.

"Ugh, an ant! Why are you watching that?" wondered Amanda.

"I'm not just watching it. I'm considerin' it."

"What's that? Considerin'?"

John liked to keep his little sister questioning. "Something my teacher told me to do."

"Why?" asked Amanda.

" 'Cause the Bible says we're supposed to," answered John.

"The Bible? Are you sure?" Amanda asked.

"Yes!" insisted John. For once he took his eyes off the ant and stared at Amanda. "Yes! It does! A wise man named Solomon in the Bible told the people they should consider an ant. So that means we should too."

His little speech convinced Amanda. She seated herself on the sidewalk beside John. "Now show me how to consider them."

"You have to do that yourself. I can't do it for you."

"But, how?" questioned Amanda. "Tell me . . . how do you consider an ant?"

John continued to watch the ants intently. Finally he heeded her questions. "You watch them. You think about what they're doin' and why they're doin' it. It's kinda like studying them and then learnin' a lesson from them."

Amanda's eyes widened. "Look," she said, pointing to a black ant. "What's it doing? It's carrying something almost as big as itself!"

"Sure," answered John. "They are very strong. They can carry things many times heavier than themselves. That's a worker ant."

"What's a worker ant?" wondered Amanda.

John was pleased that she asked the question. After all, he knew quite a bit more about ants since he had studied about them this past year in fifth grade. So he went on to explain, "Worker ants do the jobs in the ant nest or colony like helping to build nests and gathering food for themselves and for other ants. Some of the worker ants clean the nests. And some of them lick the ant eggs until they hatch and then act like nurses for the little ants, or ant grubs, as they're called."

"Oh," shrieked Amanda. "There's one crawling up my leg!"

John didn't seem worried. "Then you can get a closer look at it," he said casually.

Although Amanda didn't relish the idea of an ant crawling up her leg, she did take a closer look. She saw the ant had a head with two huge eyes and two hairy feelers on top. The ant had no ears or nose. The hard shell-like body was in two parts.

But Amanda could stand the crawly ant no longer. She swished it to the ground with her hand.

"Aw," said John. "You maybe could've seen its scissor jaws if you would have looked longer."

"Scissor jaws?" wondered Amanda.

"Yes, they dig with them, and bite and tear and chew. That's what they use to dig tunnels in the ground or in wood."

"Do they live in the ground?" wondered Amanda.

"Yes, anywhere it's dark, even in the stem of a plant," said John. "Do you see all these ants walking in a line, following each other?"

"Yes," said Amanda as she squatted close to the ant trail. "Why do they do that?"

"Because one ant, a worker ant, was out looking for

food. After it found that piece of watermelon rind, it returned to the nest, leaving an odor trail by touching its stomach to the ground again and again. That way the other ants could find the watermelon, too, and help to store it away for their future meals."

Amanda was fascinated. "Do ants always work together?" she wondered.

"Always! An ant can't live by itself. Ants live like a family, and each ant has a job to do. Around the nest are soldier ants that attack any enemies that come. They bite, sting, or squirt a smelly acid if something threatens their nest. Inside the nest is the queen ant which lays the eggs. So you see, every ant in the colony is always busy, helping each other. Watch, when I lift this board."

Amanda jumped to her feet and squealed with laughter and surprise. Hundreds of ants scattered here and there, hurrying frantically this way and that. The ant colony was in danger and each ant sensed the emergency.

"John! Amanda! Come here," called Mother. "What are you doing?"

John and Amanda raced to the kitchen door. Amanda wanted to be the first to tell. "We were considerin' an ant," reported Amanda.

Mother laughed. "My two children, if you've been considerin' the ants, you both know how important it is for each member of our family 'colony' to do his and her job. John, go pick a box of strawberries for lunch, and Amanda, set the table."

John and Amanda looked disappointed, but then remembered that considerin' an ant meant not only watching ants, it meant learning a lesson from them.

16. Wonderfully Made

"I will praise thee; for I am fearfully and wonderfully made" (Psalm 139:14a).

Do you praise God for the way you are made? Many of us seldom even think about our bodies. We may when we have a tummy ache or a sore throat. We might if we sprain a wrist or an ankle. Usually our bodies tick along smoothly without us even thinking about them.

We use our hands for almost everything we do. Our voices talk and sing as we want them to. Our eyes can see and our feet can walk or jog.

But let's take a closer look. Consider your feet, for example. You have two of them. Five pretty pink toes attached to each foot help you walk. But tell me, how is your foot made so that you can stand on it? Hop with it? Skip and run? Ride a skateboard?

The sign in the shoe store said, "Your foot has 26 bones." Twenty-six bones all working together! Besides the bones, there are muscles, veins, tendons and other parts especially designed by God so that your foot can do the work He planned for it to do. Maybe you won't mind that your foot is exceptionally wide, when you think of what a good job it is doing for you.

What about your blood circulation? You wouldn't jab your skin with a needle just to see a droplet of blood that is traveling through your body. But the encyclopedia tells us this liquid passes through 100,000 miles of "pipeline" to all parts of your body. Your heart makes the blood move or circulate.

Ask your parents or your teacher to help you feel your pulse. Do you feel a thump-thump? Your heart pumping blood causes that thump. Your heart works like Daddy's water pump, although it's much smaller in size. It's about the size of your fist. Listen and count. An adult's heart beats about *seventy* times in one minute. That is more than 100,000 times in one day! So not only did God make your heart, but He keeps it going.

How are your eyes made? I've been told there are little camera-like parts inside them that help you see wooly lambs, tiny ants, brightly colored flowers and sunsets, and the words printed in this book.

81

Each tiny part of your whole body works together marvelously. That's why we don't think about how smoothly our hearts tick or our legs move. When we're healthy we forget our ears are hearing for us. But even worse, we forget to thank God for good health. We don't remember how we're made or thank Him for it. He did such a good job of designing us in the first place, plus He keeps us going.

And besides, sometimes we may even complain about how He made us. Maybe you don't like the color of your hair or your smattering of freckles. Do you wish you were taller or shorter? Perhaps you gain a few pounds more quickly than your friend does. But the sooner you learn to appreciate the body or temple God gave you for your soul, the happier you'll be.

The thumbprint on your birth certificate will always be different from anyone else's. God made you special. And you should praise Him for it. David, the shepherd, did. He said, "I will praise thee; for I am fearfully and wonderfully made: marvellous are thy works; and that my soul knoweth right well" (Psalm 139:14).

Will you praise or will you forget?

Perhaps the following poem can help you remember.

The World Is Mine

Today, upon a bus I saw
   A lovely maid with golden hair;
I envied her—she seemed so gay—
   And, oh, I wished I were so fair.
When suddenly she rose to leave,
   I saw her hobble down the aisle;
She had one foot, and wore a crutch—
   But as she passed, she had a smile!

82

Oh, God, forgive me when I whine;
   I have two feet! The world is mine!

And when I stopped to buy some sweets,
   The lad who served me had such charm;
He seemed to radiate good cheer;
   His manner was so kind and warm.
I said, "It's so nice to deal with you.
   Such courtesy I seldom find."
He turned and said, "Oh, thank you, Sir!"
   And then I saw that he was blind!

Oh, God, forgive me when I whine;
   I have two eyes! The world is mine!

Then walking down the street I saw
   A little boy with eyes of blue.
He stood and watched as others played;
   It seemed he knew not what to do.
I stopped a moment; then I said,
   "Why don't you join the others, dear?"
He looked ahead without a word,
   And then I knew he could not hear!

Oh, God, forgive me when I whine;
   I have two ears! The world is mine!

With feet to take me where I'd go—
With eyes to see the sunset's glow—
With ears to hear what I should know—

Oh, God, forgive me when I whine;
I'm blessed indeed! The world is mine!

—Author Unknown

17. Changed on a Tree Stump

Not again! Another correction, thought Richard. *Is this what the whole summer is going to be like?*

Richard had looked forward to helping his father on their dairy farm following his third year in school. But, even more important, he had planned to have free time.

Lots of free time to do things he felt like doing. Things like riding bike, playing with Rover, and swinging on the big swing in the haymow were his favorites.

"Richard, I don't expect you to grumble every time I tell you to do something," scolded Daddy. "You have gotten into a habit of grumbling. It doesn't make life pleasant for you or for those about you."

Richard cast his eyes downward and kicked at one of the stones on the gravel driveway. He wished Daddy would keep quiet. It was true that maybe he complained more than the rest of the family, but after all, he was only a third grader going on fourth.

Daddy was continuing in spite of the fact that Richard felt he had said enough. "Do I complain? Is that where you learn it?" asked Daddy.

"No," answered Richard.

"Do you wish I would?" asked Daddy.

"No," Richard answered. "Once I'm your age I won't either. Then I'll like to work."

"Richard," said Daddy, "if you don't plan to despise work and be a grumbler when you're my age, there's no better time than now to begin working on it. When you get to be my age, it is mighty difficult to break a bad habit. And the older you get, the harder it is."

Richard couldn't imagine that. Why Daddy could do most anything. Surely breaking a silly little habit like grumbling wouldn't be hard to do for a big man like Daddy.

Daddy was still talking. "Grumbling is a serious thing. Not only is it unpleasant for the one who murmurs; it is unkind to those around the grumbler. But even more important, God dislikes the habit of grumbling. Many people in the Bible were punished for their grumbling. The Bible tells us, 'Do all things without murmurings and disputings.'"

Richard glanced up. *Why, Daddy's face looks almost sad,* he thought. *Surely my habit isn't that bad! Not at my age at least.*

Just then cousin Daryl drove in the driveway and brought his car to a halt beside Richard and Daddy. How welcome his presence was! His coming stopped the conversation abruptly.

Nineteen-year-old Daryl was Richard's favorite cousin. He often helped out on the farm, evenings and Saturdays. He was pleasant to be around, always happy and willing to give a helping hand.

"I thought I could work on sawing up that firewood tonight, if you want me to," offered Daryl.

"Yes. I'd be glad if that would be done. Richard can go along up to the woods and help stack it on the trailer as you cut it," said Daddy.

"Aww—"

Daddy's look stopped Richard before he even got started.

Soon Richard was busy stacking the wood as fast as Daryl was sawing the limbs. They chatted little because of the noise of the chain saw. But after a while, Daryl stopped the saw and said, "Let's take a little break."

Of course, this was music to Richard's ears. He was ready for a break anytime, anywhere.

They sat side by side on a tree stump. Daryl seemed exceptionally quiet, lost in deep thoughts. Richard didn't say anything either, waiting to see why Daryl was so quiet.

Finally Daryl spoke. "I was just thinking. One time when I was about your age and my father was still living, he and I took a walk over here. I had a bad habit of grumbling at that time. So one evening just before sunset we took a walk here in your woods."

Richard listened intently. Daryl grumbling? He couldn't imagine that!

Daryl continued to speak, almost as though he were thinking out loud. "He told me to find an oak tree about my height. I found one. Then he told me to pull it out by the roots. I couldn't understand why, but I did as he told me to. I struggled awhile . . . but I got it out. Then as he leaned against that maple tree over there, he said, 'Now go find another oak tree about my size.' I whistled to him when I found one as tall as he was."

What will Daryl say next? wondered Richard as Daryl paused.

"Father walked over to where I had found the father-size tree. 'Now pull it out by the roots,' he told me. 'I can't,' I told him. 'You haven't tried,' he said. 'Take a hold of the trunk and pull.' I put my arms around that tree trunk and used all the strength I had, but of course I couldn't budge it. 'Pull harder,' Father said. 'I can't,' I said." Daryl paused trying to remember the details of that evening with his father.

"Father asked me then why I couldn't pull it out and I told him the tree was too big. It was rooted too deeply. 'Son,' said Father, 'that's just how it is with habits, both good and bad. It's hard to change when you get to be my age. So it is important to let only good habits grow when you are young. That's exactly why I'm so concerned about that grumbling habit of yours, Daryl.' " Here Daryl's voice faltered. "Just a short time after that Father was killed in an accident. Ever since, I've tried to weed out bad habits before they get too deeply rooted. And I just hope someday I can be the kind of father to my children that my father was to me. He taught me such a valuable lesson."

Richard looked over at Daryl just as Daryl was wiping a tear. For awhile they both sat silently engrossed in their own thoughts. Meanwhile Richard decided two things. First, he'd get rid of the grumbling habit before it rooted any deeper. Second, from now on he'd appreciate his father who cared enough to correct him.

"Say, we've been sitting here longer than I thought," said Daryl as he checked his watch. "We'd better get to sawing."

With these words Daryl returned to his job, unaware of the change that had taken place in Richard's life there on the tree stump.

18. The Smudges That Wouldn't Budge

"Bang, bang, bang," the busy hammers sounded. The noise of the carpenters was becoming rather monotonous for the children. For a week now the fix-up men had been putting aluminum siding on the Zimmermans' house.

"Mother, what can we do?" asked seven-year-old

Loren. "We must stay out of the back yard, so we can't play on the swing, and there's nothing else to do."

Nine-year-old Lynette came up with an idea. "May we play house under the grape arbor?"

"No. I'm sorry. You'll be in the workmen's way there too." Mother's knife continued to snip the ends off the beans as she thought. "I have an idea. When I'm finished with these beans, I'll put the card table on the front porch. Then you two can color while Lisa takes her nap. It should be nice and cool there."

The front porch proved to be a relaxing spot on the warm July day. Lynette and Loren each colored several pictures. Then Loren began cutting pictures from an old magazine, and Lynette practiced writing her name with the markers. Next she doodled and drew stick people, trees, and flowers.

Two-year-old Lisa, awake from her afternoon nap, joined them on the porch and happily played with her toys.

"Oops," said Lynette. "My marker slipped off the paper and I made a mark on the card table. I hope it will come off or Mother will be unhappy." She tried to rub the spot with her fingers but the smudge didn't come off.

Loren, eager to help Lynette out of her predicament, offered, "I'll go get a cloth to wipe it." He returned, carrying the household cleaner as well. He squeezed a big squirt of cleaner on the spot and rubbed. The mark disappeared.

"Oh good! Loren, I'm glad you got it off!" exclaimed Lynette. "That means we could make marks *anywhere* and we can rub them off again!"

"Better not," advised Loren. "Mother wouldn't want you to."

"She wouldn't care as long as we wipe them off again," said Lynette. She looked about for a nice clean spot to write and draw on. There it was! On the front of the house on the new siding. She took her two favorite colors, rose and green, and squatted on the porch floor. How pretty and bright her drawing looked against the light gray siding!

Loren seated himself on the porch and observed Lynette's art talent. He looked forward to being able to write and draw like his sister could.

After drawing numerous letters, flowers, and curlicues, Lynette sat back, pleased with her artwork. She scribbled in a blue cloud yet and then decided it was time to "erase." "Now you may rub it off, Loren, while I put the caps on the markers."

Loren squirted the cleaner on the new siding. He squeezed and squirted until he had the artwork and himself well-drenched. Next he took the cloth and rubbed and rubbed. He rubbed some more. The lines smudged but that was all. He rubbed harder. They faded somewhat. But the smudges just wouldn't come off. "Lynette, they won't come off!"

"Sure they will. Rub harder. Or here, give me the cloth and I'll get them off." Lynette took the cloth and scrubbed the wall. But the smudges would not budge!

Loren felt sorry for his sister. He knew she was in trouble. *Well,* he decided, *I won't be a tattletale.*

"Let's quickly gather up our things and put them away so Mother doesn't come out here on the porch," directed Lynette. "Maybe she won't see it until it fades away, or maybe she'll think Lisa did it."

In a short time they had the crayons, books, markers, and table gathered up and tucked away neatly in their proper places.

Mother was surprised with their unusual neatness and promptness in putting their things away, but she thought nothing more of it. She told them to set the table, and they willingly cooperated.

On the outside the children appeared happy, but on the inside they were filled with fear.

Mother turned to the door, "Now I'll get Lisa and wash her up so she's ready for supper." When she returned, Lynette and Loren knew she had noticed. She looked very disappointed. "Lynette, did you write on the wall with your markers?" she questioned.

"No," lied Lynette.

"Did you, Loren?" asked Mother.

"No," he answered, then added, "Lynette didn't either." He didn't want to see his sister punished.

Lisa squirmed in Mother's arms and giggled. She pointed her pudgy hand toward the porch and babbled, "Net, Net, pretty. Net, Net, pretty."

Oh! The children had forgotten that Lisa had been observing too. And although she couldn't pronounce Lynette's name, she was telling the truth.

"Is Lisa telling the truth?" asked Mother.

Lynette started crying and answered, "Yes."

"Then you'll both need to be punished. Lynette, because of your actions and for telling an untruth," said Mother.

"But why me?" asked Loren. "I didn't make the smudges."

"No, you didn't make the smudges, but you were a false witness. And the Bible says a false witness, or a person that doesn't say the truth about another's actions, shall be punished. There is Daddy now. Tell him what each of you have done."

Daddy also was unhappy, because the carpenters

would need to insert a new sheet of siding to get rid of the smudges that wouldn't budge. But even more he was sorry that his daughter had lied and his son had been a false witness.

19. Wesley and the Winslows

Nine-year-old Wesley surveyed the flower beds. Almost all of them were mulched. He was glad he had stuck to the job instead of going with Mother.

Being the friendly person he was, Wesley would have enjoyed accompanying Mother to the new neighbors.

But when Mother had asked, "Do you want to go along to take the cake to the Winslows?" he had hesitated but for a moment.

"No, thanks. I'll finish up this job. I know you and Father would both like to have this done," he had answered.

Mother had smiled, then added, "Thanks, Wesley. I'd appreciate that! I thought I'd give you the chance. I'm sure there'll be more opportunities for you to get acquainted with our new neighbors."

Mother had then headed up the hill to the huge restored stone mansion. She had carried her token of welcome: a moist layer cake smothered with butter cream frosting swirls. Among the swirls, purple violets dotted the cake and lavender letters artistically spelled out: W-E-L-C-O-M-E.

As Wesley worked, he kept thinking about Mother meeting the folks who had moved in next door. Not much was known about them except that Doctor Winslow was coming from a big city in New Jersey to practice at the local hospital. Would they be sociable? Would they be neighborly?

Wesley did not need to wait long to gain his first impression.

Mother returned surprisingly soon.

"Back already?" Wesley asked.

"Yes. That didn't take long," answered Mother.

Wesley pried her with questions, but Mother didn't have much to say. As a Christian, Mother guarded her tongue wisely. If she couldn't speak kindly about someone, she didn't like to speak at all.

Wesley soon sensed there was no point in more questions. She must have gotten a cold reception.

Months rolled by. Wesley's family waved when the

Winslows passed, but the Winslows didn't seem to notice.

Then winter came and blew in a real old-fashioned blizzard. Wesley's father was busy scraping the driveway. When he had finished, in spite of the wind and cold, he said, "I'm going to offer to clear the Winslows' drive. Perhaps Dr. Winslow needs to get out to go to the hospital."

When Father returned from the Winslows, he wore the same disappointed expression Mother had when she had delivered the cake.

"What did they say?" asked Wesley.

"They told me I don't need to bother," Father answered soberly. "They said they can take care of themselves.

"We need to allow the Winslows their privacy," Father decided. "But we still need to show Christian courtesy, and if they're ever in need, we'll respond as neighbors should. Perhaps the Lord will arrange more ways for us to show them God's love."

Winter changed to spring and spring to summer.

Wesley, now a year older, became responsible for the mowing. He was delighted. He loved to mow. And since their large lawn bordered the Winslows', mowing afforded him weekly opportunities to observe what was going on next door. He didn't mean to be nosy, but the Winslows' independence intrigued him.

One day as Wesley was mowing close to the Winslows' property line, the riding mower began to sputter. "Out of gas!" Wesley muttered aloud as he shut down the throttle and turned off the ignition.

Just then he noticed the Winslows' Mercedes pulling to a stop in their driveway. As he stepped off the mower and removed the lid on the gas tank, he saw petite Mrs.

Winslow getting out of the car, followed by an even more petite white poodle. Groomed to perfection, the dog wore a pink ribbon around its neck.

"Fiji, go on," ordered Mrs. Winslow. But Fiji barked excitedly and frisked about Mrs. Winslow's feet as she carried packages toward the large deck.

Much as Wesley would have enjoyed watching more, he remembered his manners, turned, and started toward the utility shed for more gasoline.

Suddenly, he heard a scream. "Fiji!"

Wesley whirled in time to see Mrs. Winslow toppling to the deck steps. The packages she was carrying went flying, scattering their contents over the steps and deck. Mrs. Winslow shrieked again and moaned.

For a moment Wesley stood rooted to the spot. But Mrs. Winslow's pathetic cries and moans convinced him she was hurt.

He raced across the lawn, up the driveway, and over to where Mrs. Winslow lay.

Her face was ashen white. Above her left eye was an ugly cut, but she moaned and pointed to her ankle. It was twisted at a weird angle. All about her lay cubed ham, Swiss cheese wedges, and thick slices of roast beef.

Fiji danced and barked wildly.

"Put him . . . in the garage," Mrs. Winslow groaned. "And can you . . . call the paramedics? Oh, it hurts!"

"Where is your phone, Mrs. Winslow?" asked Wesley as he opened the service door to the garage and coaxed Fiji inside.

"Just inside the patio door . . . on the right . . . is a cordless phone. Dial 911."

Wesley was grateful his parents had taught him how to use the emergency number. He had no trouble explaining the location to the man who answered the phone.

"May I call my mother and ask her to come over?" Wesley asked Mrs. Winslow when he returned.

"Sure." Mrs. Winslow seemed to be getting her breath back, but she was obviously in pain. "Then could you bring the first aid kit from the hallway cupboard?" she asked.

In a short time, Mother arrived and helped Wesley apply gauze pads to the cut over Mrs. Winslow's eye.

"We were going to have guests this evening," Mrs. Winslow explained. "I was just carrying this snack up the deck stairs and tripped over Fiji. Oh, my ankle!" She tried to sit up but soon gave up.

"Here," said Mother, "will this cushion help?" She offered a cushion from a chair on the deck.

"Thank you," Mrs. Winslow breathed.

"I hear the ambulance coming," Mother said. "Is there anything else we can do? Wesley can clean up this meat and cheese."

"Oh, thank you," said Mrs. Winslow. "Just take home what is in the packages and throw the rest away. Could I ask you to do one more favor?"

"Sure," Mother said.

"Would you please call my husband at the office so he can meet me at the hospital?"

"I'll be glad to," Mother replied, and she went for the phone.

After the ambulance left, Mother and Wesley picked up the food, returned the first aid kit, closed the doors, and walked back toward their own home.

"Wesley, it's good you were mowing today," said Mother.

"I know," Wesley agreed.

"Did you see her fall, or how did you know she was in trouble?" asked Mother.

"The mower ran out of gas. I saw her come home, but

I was walking toward the shed to get more gas, when I heard her scream."

"You know, Son, God had things timed just right. If you had been mowing, you couldn't have heard Mrs. Winslow. And unless you would have seen her fall, you wouldn't have realized anything was wrong. She could have suffered a long time before someone discovered her."

"I never thought of that," Wesley said.

"Remember what Father said: 'Maybe the Lord will arrange more ways for us to show them God's love'? I think we are seeing the Lord's hand in this."

"Think this will change them?" asked Wesley.

"We'll certainly hope so. Seeing the Lord's hand in allowing you to find Mrs. Winslow, we can believe that He is working in their hearts as well."

Later that evening a phone call confirmed what Mother had said.

A man's deep voice spoke. "Hello. This is Doctor Winslow. I just want to personally thank you and your son for helping my wife. We certainly are fortunate having neighbors like you. My wife will probably be hospitalized for several days, but once she is feeling better, we'd like to get acquainted."

Mother expressed concern for Mrs. Winslow and said she and her family would like to know them better too.

"Is there anything else we can do?" she asked.

"Not that I can think of at the moment," replied Dr. Winslow. "But I sincerely appreciate your offer."

The conversation soon ended, and Mother turned to Wesley and Father. "That was our new neighbor calling."

"New neighbor?" asked Wesley.

"Yes, I believe the new Winslows will be different from the former Winslows." Mother smiled.

20. "Who's Next, Please?"

Gilbert entered the ice cream shop parking lot, parked his bicycle, then took his place at the end of a long line of customers.

Sweat dotted his suntanned forehead as his eyes scanned the advertisements posted in the windows.

As slowly as the line was moving, he had plenty of time to decide which frozen treat to order.

The poster promoting a new ice-cream dessert was most convincing. Which flavor should it be? The tropical fruit sounded most refreshing. That's what he'd order.

Gilbert stepped forward as the line slowly moved ahead. By now, others had fallen in line behind him.

After a while, the gentleman behind Gilbert, who had been rather impatiently jingling the change in his pocket said, "Excuse me. Did you ever have any of those desserts?"

Gilbert turned to the silver-haired stranger and answered politely, "Not yet. But I'm going to try one today. It says they're cold. That will be great on such a warm day."

The gentleman stroked his chin and then nodded in agreement. "Yes, it is warm. And you look especially warm. Been working hard? Mowing lawn, perhaps?"

"That's right. My grandma's. I've been mowing her yard all summer. Since this is the last week before school starts, she gave me money to stop by for ice cream on my way home."

"That's nice," replied the gentleman, then motioned Gilbert on toward the service window. "I believe it's your turn to order now."

Gilbert stepped up to the window just as a tousle-haired boy stepped in front of him.

"Who's next?" asked the waitress.

"I am," said the newcomer.

The waitress looked from Gilbert to the other boy and then back again.

Stunned, Gilbert shrugged his shoulders and gave the waitress a puzzled look.

"Who's next, please?" the waitress repeated. Her voice

revealed the irritation she felt by the delay. Obviously, she thought Gilbert was next.

"A banana split and a small cola," ordered the newcomer as he pretended he hadn't even seen Gilbert.

Gilbert was dumbfounded by such bold cheating. "I—" He meant to tell the waitress, "I was next!" But instead, Gilbert checked his tongue and said, "Go ahead with his order."

But inside, Gilbert continued to struggle. One side of him raged, "It's not fair! What an unkind, disrespectful thing to do!" But a calmer voice reasoned, "As a Christian, Gilbert, you must not strike back. How would Jesus respond?"

That softened Gilbert, but he still felt a little irritated.

After the boy received his banana split, he cast a sideways smirk at Gilbert. "You're next!" He chuckled, then sauntered away as boldly as he had come.

While Gilbert waited for his dessert, the gentleman behind him said, "You're from a Christian home, aren't you?"

"Why, yes," answered Gilbert, curious why he asked that question.

"I thought so," the gentleman continued. "The way you responded when you were wronged told me you have parents who are trying to teach you the right way. I had parents like that too. But I failed them and the God they serve. Don't ever make the same mistake I did, Sonny."

At that moment the waitress arrived with Gilbert's order. "Who's next, please?" she asked.

Abruptly their conversation ended and the gentleman stepped forward to place his order.

Gilbert walked away carrying the cold cup in his hand, but his heart felt warm. He was humbled as well, for he knew not all his thoughts had been good. He had been tempted to forsake his parents' teaching.

"Dear Lord, help me not to fail them," Gilbert breathed. "Or You either."

21. Dale's Dirty Dishes

Dale flipped through the stack of recipe cards. "Where is a frosting recipe?" he wondered. "I know Mother always whips up the icing without a recipe. But that's not me. I'm a boy!"

"I'm a boy" was a phrase Mother had heard quite often. That was until Daddy reminded Dale that boys and men eat too.

"Dale," Daddy had said, "there's no way Mother can keep us hungry men fed without our help. We're a hungry bunch, you know. She always did the kitchen work before. But, now that the twins came, she'll need help."

Dale made no comment, for he knew it was true that Mother did need help.

Daddy looked directly into his eleven-year-old son's eyes. "Dale, are you willing to be that help? Daniel is older than you and accustomed to helping me outside. Little David at five years old can't help a lot in the kitchen, you know. Will you, Dale?" he asked again.

"Yes," answered Dale, as he glanced downward.

"Good!" exclaimed Daddy. "I'm thankful God gave us food to eat and prepare. And I'm thankful God gave me a son who's willing to help with that important work." Then with a pat on Dale's shoulder, he left to go about his barn chores.

What Daddy doesn't understand, thought Dale, *is that my lips said yes, but my heart and head haven't fully agreed yet.* But Dale set out to fulfill his responsibilities nonetheless.

After the third cookie, Dale decided his cookies had turned out reasonably well. Now the frosting. . . .

Following the frosting recipe wasn't all that hard, and putting the frosting on was kind of fun. True, some of the cookies were smothered with icing and others had just a bit on. But at last the cookies were all frosted.

"Now, may I go outside?" Dale asked.

Mother, who was rocking both Dwight and Dwayne at once, glanced at the clock. "No, Dale. It's time to start peeling potatoes for dinner. And then maybe you can clean up the sink and wash those dishes before dinner so you won't have as many afterwards."

Dale glanced at the clock and then at the sink.

Dishes! he thought. *I just washed the breakfast dishes. Then I made the cookies, and already there's a whole stack of dishes again.*

He surveyed the countertop. He had no idea he had used so many bowls, spoons, spatulas, measuring cups, and cookie sheets. And by the looks of the empty flour canister, it needed a washing. What had he splashed on the sugar canister? It, too, needed a wiping. Oh, and the mixer! Dishes! The more Dale looked, the more he seemed to see.

Dutifully, he began to peel potatoes. He got out a kettle to hold the peeled potatoes. *That will be one more dish,* Dale calculated. *And then there's the dishpan of peelings and one more paring knife. If I brown butter for the potatoes, that will make one more saucepan to wash. Maybe we'll mash them instead. Oh, no! That would mean a mixing bowl and beaters to wash then. Probably the milk pitcher would get empty then and need to be washed too.*

By now Dale's dirty-dishes count had made him quite glum. Besides, as soon as he'd have the counter cleaned up and dinner made, there would be more stacks.

Guess I'll peel one more potato, decided Dale. *And then I'll start washing dishes to make room for more.*

He opened the hot water faucet full blast and squirted more than enough liquid soap into the sink. As he flung the dishcloth into the suds, his eyes caught the soap label's promise: "Helps hands stay soft and young looking."

Definitely not meant for boys' hands! decided Dale.

106

Won't I have the nicest, softest, whitest boys' hands you ever did see?

Sweat dripped down his forehead. *Washing dishes is certainly a warm job,* he concluded as he opened the sink window a bit further.

What was that neatly printed paper saying attached to the frame between the windows? Dale's eyes scanned Mother's handwritten sign.

"In everything give thanks," the letters stated.

In everything? thought Dale. *In dishwater, even? Does that mean me? Women and girls could probably be thankful in dishwater.*

Daddy's voice startled Dale. "So you're doing the fun . . . no maybe I should say the important job of washing dishes?"

Dale noticed Daddy reach for a frosted cookie.

Daddy continued, "You know, Dale, the Bible even mentions men wiping dishes."

"It does?" asked Dale.

"Yes, it says the Lord will wipe Jerusalem as a man wipeth a dish, wiping it, and turning it upside down."

Dale was astounded. He had no idea God would use a man wiping dishes as a Biblical example.

"These cookies are delicious," complimented Daddy.

"Thanks," said Dale with a smile, "and just maybe I should change my thinking about baking and washing dishes. I guess it's not a girls-only job after all."

22. Melissa Finds Comfort

"Mother, what can I do? There is no one to play with. I miss Timmy so much! It's so quiet!"

With these words, Melissa burst into sobs. During the funeral and the week since Timmy was buried, Melissa had used all the strength and courage a ten-year-old could muster. Now she was exhausted.

Darting from the kitchen, she flung herself onto the living room sofa. The cushion she clutched absorbed some of the tears which flowed uncontrollably.

Out on the kitchen counter a German chocolate cake stood half frosted. Mother stuck the spatula into the frosting bowl. She reached into her apron pocket for her handkerchief. It took a few moments until her own tears were dabbed away.

Melissa heard Mother's footsteps coming closer. Now she felt Mother's arm gently around her as Mother sat on the edge of the sofa beside her. Neither spoke.

Except for the clock's tick-tock and Melissa's crying, the house was quiet.

More minutes ticked by. Melissa's sobbing grew softer now. Her grip on the pillow became more relaxed.

After clearing her throat, Mother began. "Melissa."

"What?" managed Melissa.

"Do you think Timmy is happy today?" questioned Mother.

"Yes."

"Why?"

"Well," Melissa replied, "he's in heaven with Jesus."

"That's right. He is. It must be so wonderful to be there. Wouldn't it be a joy for our whole family to be there?"

"Yes," sniffed Melissa. "Why couldn't we all go? I miss him so, and I'd like to be there myself."

"Well, Melissa, first of all, do you believe God had a reason for calling Timmy home?"

"I guess so. Brother Allen said so in the funeral sermon anyway." She turned her head sideways on the pillow so she could hear Mother better. She noticed

Mother's cheeks were wet too.

Again Mother cleared her throat before she talked. "I know we can't understand why Timmy's death came so soon. But when we realize what follows death for Christians, we can have joy. It is really going home for us. And we must have faith in God that He knows far better than we do when to call someone home."

"Isn't there something in the Bible like that? Some verse about God's thoughts being better than ours?" asked Melissa.

"Yes, there is. Let's look for it," replied Mother as she rose to get her Bible. "It's in Isaiah, about the fifty-fifth chapter."

Melissa sat up and wiped tears from her eyes. Mother sat beside her. Leafing through the Bible, Mother paused at Isaiah 55. She scanned the chapter, then read verses eight and nine. "For my thoughts are not your thoughts, neither are your ways my ways, saith the LORD. For as the heavens are higher than the earth, so are my ways higher than your ways, and my thoughts than your thoughts."

Melissa took a deep breath, then sighed. Mother silently reread the verses. They were such a reassurance to her too.

"But, why, even if we know it's best and God's will and all, why do we miss him so? Is it wrong for me to cry? Shouldn't we even feel sad?" Melissa wondered.

"What happened when Lazarus died? Jesus wept. He experienced the same feelings of sorrow we have now. That's why He can be such a comfort to us. He understands," Mother assured. "He went through it Himself. So it's not wrong to grieve, but we shouldn't sorrow as though we had no hope."

As Melissa sat beside Mother, she began to feel better.

110

She didn't feel as if she was alone in this. Mother and Daddy understood. But most of all, Jesus understood. It seemed like a heavy weight was rolling away. She felt more relaxed, calm, and in a way, even happy. Was this what people call comfort? It was the first time she really knew what it felt like.

"Melissa," Mother said, "it's time we get supper on. Daddy will soon be home. God will give us strength to go on, even during our time of bereavement. As Jesus' disciples, we have work to do, and we must not grow weary in doing it. Before long our time will come to reap, just like Timmy's did. Now, will you please run out to the garden and pick some tomatoes for supper?" With these words she planted a kiss on her daughter's forehead.

Melissa grabbed a dishpan from the sink. Odd. Inside she almost felt like singing.

23. Strawberry Red

"David!" Daddy's call reached David's ears in the berry patch.

David placed a bright red strawberry into the berry box as he arose and looked toward Daddy. Beads of sweat trickled down his sunburned cheeks. This was his twelfth box of berries for today. The sun beat its warm rays against David's face and neck.

"Yes, Daddy. What do you want?" called David.

"How about it? Are you ready for a break?"

"Yes! What is it?" David quickly replied. He came running toward his father. "Where are we going?" he asked as he noticed Daddy heading for the pickup.

"To the feed mill," answered Daddy. "I need some pellets and supplement. Quickly run those boxes in to Mother. I need to do some figuring before we leave."

David *did* hurry. He didn't have to be told. He automatically hurried if he got the chance to go away with Daddy, especially when it meant a break from picking strawberries.

He gathered the boxes together and carried them three at a time to the house. *Maybe vacation won't be so bad after all,* he thought as he raced to the garden for the last load. School had closed last week for the summer vacation. And David had found himself in the strawberry patch every day since, except on Sunday. Strawberry picking wasn't his favorite pastime! *Is this how vacation will be?* he had thought. *Just follow Dad's orders to work?*

Now David's heart felt lighter. Perhaps Daddy wasn't so tough after all. True, David had to work harder than most other boys eight years old. And sometimes he felt Daddy wasn't fair. But at the moment he forgot those feelings. His feet scampered to the waiting pickup.

"Ready? Set? The train's leaving the station," teased Daddy as he lightly tooted the horn. "Just made it in time, Sonny!"

David smiled at his tall, suntanned Daddy.

"Say, didn't you get all those berries into the boxes?" questioned Daddy. "Did you think you were supposed to sample them while you pick?"

"Why do you ask that?" wondered David.

"Check the mirror and you'll know why I asked."

The sun visor squeaked as David tugged at it. The mirror clipped on the visor told the answer. Big smudges of strawberry red circled his mouth.

"Mouth-watering, aren't they?" asked Daddy. He continued before David could reply. "I don't blame you for eating some. But, David, you'll need to stay in the truck at the mill. You're just too dirty to go along in."

David was disappointed. *Stay in the truck?* That wouldn't be much fun. But he didn't dare beg to go along in. Daddy's statements were final. He had learned that the hard way. Daddy expected his children to be obedient.

The click of the right turn signal announced the arrival at the mill. Daddy shifted down to second gear as the truck climbed the steep grade in the parking lot.

"Looks like the loading ramps are both full," said Daddy. "I'll just park here until I can back up to load. Meanwhile I'll pay my bill." He pulled the emergency brake, jumped out of the truck, and headed toward the mill.

David was left alone, but not for long. Burt Long and his daddy also happened to be at the mill. The Longs were close neighbors of the Weavers. But David wasn't allowed to play with Burt often. Somehow he always managed to get into mischief if Burt was around long.

"Hey, Davey, you stuck in the truck? Come on! Let's have some fun while we wait on our pappies!" yelled Burt.

"No, Burt, I'm supposed to stay in the truck. Daddy told me to," David replied.

"Aw, Davey. Ya chicken or somethin'? My pa never

114

makes me stay cooped up like that!"

This was getting to be difficult. David so much would have liked to romp with Burt, and yet he was always taught that children should obey their parents. What should he do?

Then an idea sparked in David's head. "Why don't you hop into the truck with me? We can pretend we're truck drivers. I'll pretend to drive for awhile; then you can," called David.

"Okay. Slide over then," Burt said as he pulled open the door and climbed onto the seat with his dirty cowboy boots. The door banged shut instantly because the truck was sitting on the hill.

Burt chattered on. "Don't just turn the steering wheel. Turn the key to ACC and put the wipers on."

"Won't that start the engine?"

"Nope! I tried it on my pa's truck already," replied Burt. "Put the lights on, and release that emergency brake. If you don't, I will!" threatened Burt.

Children, obey your parents. A wise son maketh a glad father. David had memorized both of those verses and they crossed his mind now. But Burt's voice sounded loud and exciting.

David's hand reached for the emergency brake. He hesitated. "What would Daddy say?" he questioned. *Oh, he'll never know,* he decided as he pulled the release.

The truck lurched backward and began to roll. Faster! Faster! Faster!

The boys screamed. David tried to press the brake, but he missed it.

On and on ... coasting down the hill ... more speed ... more speed....

"Oh no!"

"Help!"

Crash! The truck sideswiped a tree. It swerved, and then it hit the railroad bed at the bottom of the hill.

Fear, sorrow, hurt, and shame blended together and colored David's red face an even deeper red. Burt's cheeks were white as chalk.

The truck was dented and scratched. The boys, fortunately, had only a few bruises, bumps, and scratches.

But the biggest pain was in David's heart. Imagine how he felt when Daddy came running to the bottom of the hill.

24. Chester's Nose Trouble

Chester took one more look into the mirror. He didn't like at all what he saw! And the worst part was, he couldn't change it one bit! He, ten-year-old Chester, had that awfully long nose permanently.

117

"You look just like Grandpa Hoover!" he heard over and over again. Now, Grandpa Hoover was a wonderful grandfather. He radiated inner joy to everyone he met. It almost seemed Grandpa Hoover didn't even realize he had such an odd nose—long with an upswept tip.

But Chester did not want to hear "you *look* like Grandpa Hoover." *If only they'd say you act like, or you talk like, or you remind me of, Grandpa Hoover,* thought Chester. *That would be complimentary. But no, they say, "You look like him." They may as well say, "You inherited that same funny-looking nose your Grandpa has!"*

"Chester," called Mother. "Grandpa is waiting for you. Please hurry."

My look-alike is here and we're going to pick huckleberries, thought Chester as he grabbed the five-quart bucket and raced toward the waiting pickup.

"Hello, Chester. Hop in!" was Grandpa's cheerful greeting.

"Hi, Grandpa!" Chester returned.

"I've been looking forward to spending this forenoon in the woods," Grandpa began. "It seems God uses nature to teach me lessons time and again. The woods are such a delightful place to learn them. I was looking forward to spending time with you too." Grandpa grinned at Chester. "Of course, I have to admit, I don't dread the huckleberry pie Grandma will make either." Grandpa chuckled.

Yes, Grandpa's his usual jolly self, thought Chester. *You'd almost think he enjoys wrinkling up that long nose.*

The huckleberry bushes were loaded with fruit, and the buckets were soon filled.

"Now that the buckets are full, why don't we rest a bit here on this old log and breathe in some more of this clear fresh air," suggested Grandpa.

Chester liked the idea and seated himself beside his older look-alike.

Casting his eyes to the top of a stately oak tree near-by, Grandpa commented, "I'm always amazed at the variety in nature. Some trees are tall. Others remain short. Their leaves have varied shapes. The grain and the bark vary from tree to tree. God saw we'd have need for different kinds of trees. Variety also makes the land-scape more beautiful."

"Is that an apple tree over there?" questioned Chester.

"No, that's a pear tree. Amuses me you asked about that tree," smiled Grandpa. "I helped my grandpa plant that tree."

Chester glanced at Grandpa. A smile was dancing across Grandpa's wrinkled face. *Why he almost looks handsome in spite of his oversized nose,* thought Chester.

Now Grandpa reminisced. "I remember the lesson my grandpa taught me that day."

Chester listened intently.

"I was having a problem accepting how God made me. I had lots of nose trouble as a boy. Not nosy and minding other's business. I mean trouble accepting my extraordi-narily long nose. Did a fine job of smelling, but I thought no one else in the world was doomed to live a life with such a face."

Chester was spellbound. *So Grandpa Hoover does realize the middle of his face is unusual! Poor man,* thought Chester. *He's suffered all this time. Seventy some years!*

"What a valuable lesson he taught me that day," con-tinued Grandpa. "He told me how each tree and each snowflake is unique. He told me God has a purpose and plan for everything He creates. God makes the different birds sing and they *all* contribute their sounds to the woodland's song. 'That's what God planned for each of His creatures,' he'd say. 'But so often we human creatures don't accept ourselves as God made us. We fret over what we don't have, instead of being glad for talents God gave us.'"

Chester listened further.

"I told my grandpa, 'I sure can't accept my nose.' But he informed me as long as I'm thinking about my nose, I'm not thinking of God or others. He told me as long as I focus my attention on my nose I won't be happy. I decided right then to quit worrying about my nose. The Bible tells us even Jesus wasn't lovely to look upon, yet He was the best Friend anyone could ever have."

"That's a new idea for me," said Chester. "I've been having nose trouble myself."

Grandpa Hoover gave a hearty laugh. "Don't waste your time and energy. There will always be people who wish God would have made them darker, lighter, shorter, taller, thinner, fatter . . . or shorter-nosed. But watch, they're not the happy ones."

Chester nodded. He had accomplished more than picking huckleberries. He had solved his nose trouble.

25. Singing and Making Melody

Do you like to sing? A song I know says:

The birds upon the treetops sing their song;
The angels chant their chorus all day long;
The flowers in the garden blend their hue;
So why shouldn't I, why shouldn't you,
    praise Him too?

Good question, isn't it? Why shouldn't we praise Him? Singing is a way for us to praise God.

Perhaps you like to sing songs, but did you ever *write* a song?

Do you ever wonder how some songs came to be written? This story is about a songwriter named Fanny Crosby.

Fanny Crosby

John Crosby and his wife lived in a little cottage in Southeast, New York. How happy they were when on March 24, 1820, a little girl was born to them. They called her Fanny.

But before Fanny was six weeks old, her eyes became sore and inflamed. Her parents were concerned about her and had their country doctor take care of her. He put warm rags on her eyes, but that didn't help. Instead her eyes became worse. Baby Fanny became blind!

But this was not her only loss. Before Fanny was a year old she lost her father. After her daddy died, her mother and grandmother took care of her.

Poor Fanny couldn't see her family or friends. She never saw a furry kitten or dew sparkling on green grass. What could she do if she couldn't see? Could God use such a person for His good?

Friendly neighbors felt sorry for Fanny. They decided to give money so that Fanny could see a specialist who might help her. But the doctor said her eyes were hopeless.

The Crosby family moved to Ridgefield, Connecticut. Here Fanny liked to spend time outdoors by herself. One day nine-year-old Fanny went out into the field by herself. She thought of her life and her future. Then she asked God to use her for good.

After she got home, her heart was happy and she made up a poem. It said:

> Oh, what a happy soul am I,
> Although I cannot see;
> I am resolved that in this world
> Contented I will be,
> How many blessings I enjoy
> That other people don't,
> To weep and sigh because I'm blind
> I cannot and I won't.

What beautiful words for a blind child of nine to write! God certainly could use her life to help others.

Like all children, Fanny needed schooling. At the age of twelve, she entered the New York City School for the Blind. When she enrolled as a student, she didn't realize she would later come back as a teacher. Fanny became a good friend of the secretary of the school. Later this secretary, Grover Cleveland, became President of the United States.

When Fanny grew older, she married a blind man called Alexander Van Alstyne, also a teacher. Her name changed, but she continued to use Fanny Crosby to sign the songs she was writing.

And write she did! She wrote over *seven thousand* hymns until the time she died at the age of ninety-five! No other person ever wrote as many hymns as she did.

Do you know the song "Safe in the Arms of Jesus"? The words to that song were written in less than a half hour. William Doane knocked on Fanny's door one afternoon. He and Fanny often worked together on songs. She would write the words; he would write the music.

This time he had a tune ready. "Listen closely," he said, "because my train leaves in thirty-five minutes and I want to take that new hymn with me when I go."

He became rather impatient and feared she wouldn't have it written in time. But Fanny went to her desk and wrote line after line. To her the music suggested the thought of Deuteronomy 33:27, "Underneath are the everlasting arms." In fifteen or twenty minutes Fanny handed Mr. Doane the touching hymn, "Safe in the Arms of Jesus."

Do you know the song "All the Way My Saviour Leads Me"? Fanny wrote this because her heart was thankful for God's answer to one of her prayers. Fanny often prayed. In fact, she always did before she wrote a spiritual song.

But this time "Aunt Fanny," as many people called her, not only needed inspiration for a song, but she also needed money. Five dollars to be exact. Troubled about her lack of ideas and her lack of funds, she prayed. Just as she finished praying, a friend came to see her. They visited awhile. Then the friend rose to leave, shook hands, and slipped a five dollar bill into Fanny's hand!

After the friend left, Fanny thanked God for answering her need, then started writing. The words she wrote are the words we sing: "All the way my Saviour leads me. / What have I to ask beside? / Can I doubt His tender mercy, / Who through life has been my guide?"

When Fanny visited different places, God gave her thoughts and ideas for songs. One time she was at the Bowery Mission in New York City. Here many down-and-out men came to church services. She longed that these men would stop their evil habits. When she got home she wrote the song "Rescue the Perishing."

"Praise Him, Praise Him"; "Near the Cross"; "I Am

Thine, O Lord"; and "Blessed Assurance" are familiar songs that Fanny wrote. She also wrote "Though Your Sins Be As Scarlet"; "Jesus Is Calling"; "He Hideth My Soul"; and "Tell Me the Story of Jesus."

Page through a hymnbook and check in the upper left-hand corner of each song. When we see how often blind Fanny Crosby's name appears, we are challenged with what God can do through one person's life. Don't let anything undesirable in your life keep you from serving God.

26. Gone on Father's Day?

Phil Miller's brown eyes scanned the heavens as he hastily pushed the mower into the utility shed and latched the door. Next, the twelve-year-old dashed to the patio, grabbed the three lawn chairs, folded them, and set them inside the laundry door for safety.

126

Was there anything else outside that needed securing before the fury of the storm broke? Yes, Mom had hung one of Dad's suits on the line to air before packing it into his suitcase.

Each pant leg was furiously flapping in the wind like the neighbor's colorful windsock. From the line, Phil snatched the clothespins that held Dad's pants. Next he grabbed the suit coat, the coat Dad felt most comfortable in when he had to preach.

The wind was picking up momentum. The sky lighted up and that was followed closely by a clap of thunder.

The willow tree branches looked like a giant broom sweeping first this way, then that way. Faster and faster the branches whipped back and forth, back and forth. The storm was almost here.

Phil reached the laundry door just as the rain began.

At the same time, Mom, coming from the bedroom, and Dad from his study, appeared in the laundry in search of Phil. A look of relief crossed both parents' faces as they found Phil was safely inside.

"This storm came up quickly, didn't it?" asked Dad.

"It must have!" said Mom. Then she noticed what Phil was holding. "Oh, good, Phil! I'm glad you thought of getting Dad's suit! I hadn't noticed the storm was coming!"

"It did come quickly," answered Phil. "I had seen the dark clouds in the distance and I thought I would easily get the mowing done, but I barely finished in time."

Mom took the suit from Phil and went to fold it on the kitchen table.

Dad went to the west kitchen door to look out, while Phil scrubbed his grass-stained hands at the washbowl. Next he washed the dirt and perspiration from his face. Then he got his comb and looked in the mirror. The wind had played havoc with his wavy brown hair. After restoring order to his part, he looked in the mirror again.

There! That isn't bad! he decided. *I don't look too bad on the outside. But the mirror doesn't show how storm-tossed I feel on the inside.* Just then Phil's thoughts were interrupted.

A staccato beating against the windows confirmed that the storm was peppering the earth with hail.

"Hail!" said Dad. "What a blessing to have a safe, dry place to be!"

"That's right," agreed Mom.

"Yes!" Phil added. "And how nice to know we're all here. If this storm would have come tomorrow evening—"

Phil never finished his sentence. It wouldn't help to verbalize his thoughts. It would just make Mom and Dad feel bad. They had explained it to him previously. The church needed Dad. And Phil was old enough to realize Dad had no choice but to be gone on Father's Day. Now that he had been ordained bishop, he was like a father to the church people also.

Phil also knew that Dad, in spite of his love and responsibility for the church, preferred to spend more time at home. But Dad was only one person. He could do only so much. Therefore, Phil had purposed not to complain or fuss. But tonight when the storm came . . . he couldn't explain it . . . he just knew he was fearful and dreaded to have Dad gone again. How Phil wished tomorrow wouldn't take Dad away from him! But instead of blurting out his troubles, he sprawled across the recliner and said nothing.

Dad and Mom sat waiting for the storm to abate. Mom was quietly humming the tune, "Keep Me Safe Till the Storm Passes By."

Dad got up and went from window to window, checking to see whether any windows had broken and if all was well. Next he got a kerosene lantern in case the electricity would go off. He also laid the flashlight on the table.

The storm outside did not easily settle. For some time the storm seemed to hang directly above the Millers, whipping, lashing, cracking, pelting. But eventually it passed.

Then Dad rose, walked to the door and surveyed the outdoors. "The good Lord answered our prayers and kept us safe," said Dad. "But we certainly had a display of His power and might."

"Yes," agreed Mom. "And I'm so glad you were here, Dad! But, now that the storm is over, I'd better get back to packing your suitcase. If I don't, I won't have it ready when you want to leave with the other ministers for the ordination."

"I appreciate your getting it ready for me," replied Dad with a smile. "My fingers aren't great for folding clothes for a suitcase. But maybe my hands should get busy outside clearing some of the leaves and twigs the storm pruned from our trees." Then he glanced at Phil. "How about it, Phil? Will you please help me?"

Phil nodded.

Together, Dad and Phil went outside and got the rakes.

The hail had shredded some leaves on the trees, but the garden had been somewhat sheltered by the house.

As they worked, father and son shared some small talk, but after a few minutes the sun appeared and a bright rainbow shone across the sky.

"Look, Dad," said Phil, "a rainbow!"

Immediately Dad came and stood by Phil's side.

"That's beautiful!" exclaimed Dad. "It's just another

reminder that God keeps His promises. He is a wonderful Father."

"Father?" questioned Phil.

"Yes, Father!" answered Dad.

"Not like you, Dad!"

"No, better than I, Phil."

"Better? How can He be?" questioned Phil. "I can't think of a father better than you!"

"But, Phil, God is. He promised to be a Father to us. When I'm home or when I'm away, I hope you can learn to trust God as your Father. He loves you, cares for you, and protects you better than I can."

"But, but . . . Dad, He seems so far away when I'm lonely. And how can I be sure He hears my prayers? Isn't He too busy to listen to a child's prayers like mine, Dad?"

"Do you feel as though God is busy at times like telephone lines are?" asked Dad.

"Yes. How can I be sure He hears someone unimportant like me?"

"Because He told us in the Bible that if we call on Him, He will answer. That's a promise as sure as the one this rainbow stands for. And Phil, God is not like busy phone lines. He's more like . . ." Dad paused and thought. ". . . more like the air we breathe. He can be anywhere, anytime. There's a long word to describe it called *omnipresent*. It means present or active everywhere. That's how God is. When I'm away, God will hear me there, but He also will hear you and keep you and Mom safe here at home."

Phil raised his eyes and looked into the kind face of his father. "Dad," he said, "if my heavenly Father is better than my earthly father, He must be wonderful."

"Yes," assured Dad, "He is wonderful. I make many

mistakes, but our Heavenly Father doesn't. He can protect you much better than I can. And another thing. A few minutes ago you called yourself unimportant."

Phil listened.

"You are important to God and to me, Phil. And I love you and pray for you while I'm gone. Will you do the same for me, since I miss you and Mom when I'm gone?" asked Dad.

"Yes, I will! Since I know God listens anytime, I can pray often for you. Anytime! Anywhere!"

"Thank you!" said Dad. "I need that."

Phil noticed a tear had slid down Dad's cheek and now glistened in the sunlight. Somehow Phil knew there would probably be more storms ahead for him and Dad, but it meant a lot to know they both had a Father who loved them and would be with them everywhere, all the time.

27. Nosy Marilyn and Her Brother

Beth handed a neatly crayoned picture to Rosalyn who was perched on top of the stepladder. It belonged to Marilyn, the new girl in the classroom.

"Marilyn knows her art," whispered Beth as she handed two thumbtacks to Rosalyn.

Rosalyn didn't quite catch what Beth had said, but since they were privileged to hang the pictures while the others finished their tests, she thought it best not to ask Beth to repeat her statement. So she just smiled and nodded to Beth.

But Rosalyn was curious. As she tacked the picture she tried to piece together the words she had caught. "Marilyn . . . nose . . . art" she had heard. As she reached for the next picture, she glanced in Marilyn's direction. Perhaps she could figure out Beth's statement.

Marilyn had finished her test, had turned the test paper over, and was sitting contentedly watching the girls put up the artwork. She smiled at Rosalyn.

Rosalyn moved the ladder and kept thinking all the while. *Ah, now I have it,* she thought as an idea struck her. *Beth said Marilyn is nosy about art, because she's sitting there staring at us while we hang these pictures. I wonder if there's not a bit of jealousy mixed in . . . wishes she would have gotten the chance instead of us. At any rate,* Rosalyn's thoughts continued, *she's not going to get between Beth and me. Beth is such a kind person, and I want Beth as my friend.*

Recess time came. The fourth and fifth graders went out to play ball. But Rosalyn kept her eyes on Marilyn. *Is she nosy?* she wondered. Sure enough, Marilyn was talking with Marie. She must have asked Marie a question because Marie cupped her hand to her mouth and whispered something in Marilyn's ear. Both girls then laughed.

Now it was "nosy" Marilyn's turn to bat. She stepped up to the plate and on the first pitch whammed the ball into the outfield. Marilyn made it safely to second.

This was Rosalyn's opportunity. She edged up to Marie. "Marie, I have something to tell you. I guess I should say *warn* you. Don't tell Marilyn too many of your secrets. I've been told she's a nosy person. Besides, I've been watching her, and I wonder if she doesn't try to work between friends."

It was Marie's turn to bat. She didn't have a chance to discuss the matter any further, and they all were soon absorbed in the game.

That afternoon, however, Marie remembered what Rosalyn had said, and she recalled her conversation with Marilyn. Marilyn had asked if Marie could come to her house on Saturday. At first Marie had been delighted, but then she remembered. Saturday afternoon was the time her family had chosen to have a work day for their minister, Brother Baker. Marie whispered this in Marilyn's ear because Beth was the minister's daughter, and Marie had wanted this to be a surprise for Beth.

"So that's why it didn't suit Beth," Marilyn had laughed. "I asked her to come, but she told me she had to stay home Saturday. But she didn't know why."

Now Marie wondered. *Was Marilyn just trying to find out my secret? Will she tell Beth? Is she trying to work between Beth and me?* She looked over at Marilyn. Marilyn was looking at Beth. *She acts so nice to my face,* thought Marie.

On the way home from school, Marie's brother Matthew told her, "There's a new boy in my room. His name's Dwayne."

"Dwayne what?"

"Dwayne Weaver," said Matthew.

"Oh, so Marilyn has a brother. Wonder if he's like Marilyn," said Marie.

Matthew kicked at a stone. "Why, what's she like?"

134

"Marilyn?" Marie rolled her big brown eyes. "I don't think I should tell you."

"Aw, come on," Matthew said. "You imagine things. Dwayne's going to make a super friend."

Marie tossed her head. "I'm not imagining things. In one day at school the girls have already discovered that Marilyn Weaver is nosy and jealous. She is very nice to your face, but she tries to work between friends. Her brother is probably just like her. Wasn't he especially friendly to you?"

"Well, yeah," Matthew replied.

"Was he just as chummy with Lee?" Marie persisted.

Lee was Matthew's best friend. Matthew had seen Dwayne and Lee talking and laughing together. *Maybe Marie's right,* Matthew admitted to himself. He'd better warn Lee.

And so the gossip chain continued. Matthew told Lee. Lee shared it with Dale. Dale warned his sister, Nancy. Nancy was surprised, but glad for the warning. She shocked Barbara with the news, because Barbara had grown to like Marilyn by now.

On and on the story went, and it grew as it was retold. "Marilyn and Dwayne are friendly to your face, but they tell stories behind your back. Watch out. Don't tell them anything. They are two-faced. They probably moved because they weren't liked where they were. They probably had lots of fights and no friends. Maybe they were expelled from their school."

Marilyn and Dwayne felt the other students drawing away from them, but they didn't know what was wrong. The more friendly they tried to be, the more the others seemed to want to avoid them. Life at the new school became more and more miserable.

Finally, the problem reached the ears of Mr. Zimmerman, the principal. Bit by bit he unraveled the chain of gossip. In school assembly the next day he explained how gossip works. "When we start imagining evil about someone, we easily jump to wrong conclusions. Then if we tell someone else, we spread our bad thoughts around. Each time the misunderstanding is repeated, it tends to grow—like a snowball that gets bigger and bigger as it is rolled along. The more untrue the gossip becomes, the more hurtful it is for those whom we are talking about."

The students glanced nervously at Marilyn and Dwayne.

"To correct this problem," the principal continued, "I am asking all of you who have spread unkind stories about our new students to apologize to them. Tell them you are sorry, and let's see if we can make them feel welcome at our school in the days ahead."

Shame and regret were etched on many faces, and many apologies were made that day. But best of all, Marilyn and her brother were no longer considered nosy or two-faced, and the students discovered how pleasant and friendly Marilyn and Dwayne actually were.

28. The Best Part of Michelle's Day

Michelle stretched as far as her arms and legs could reach. She glanced at the alarm clock. "Oh, it is six-thirty," she noted. "Time to get up."

Knock! Knock! Someone rapped quickly on her bedroom door.

"Michelle, aren't you up yet?" questioned Michael, Michelle's ten-year-old twin brother. "Don't you know what day this is?"

"Oh, that's right!" Michelle needed no more prompting. She was dressed and downstairs in a jiffy.

Today was the day they had looked forward to most of the summer. This day at Grandma and Aunt Ruth's house promised lots of fun and excitement. This yearly just-before-school event usually consisted of a picnic and games for all the cousins, two years old and older.

Breakfast was completed, and the dishes were washed and put away in record time.

"Mother will take you over to Grandma's house," said Daddy. "Do have a nice time today, but don't forget to mind your manners. There will be quite a few children there today and not many adults. Make it an enjoyable day for Grandma and Aunt Ruth too."

"We will!" chorused Michelle and Michael.

"Good! If each of you remembers the golden rule of doing unto others as you would have them do unto you, it will be a very pleasant day."

"Okay," replied Michael.

Michelle nodded her head to show Daddy she also planned to do that.

As usual Grandma and Aunt Ruth had planned lots of things for them to do. The older ones played prisoner's base and snatch the bacon, while the younger cousins played drop the hanky and duck, duck, gray duck. Even two-year-old Beth, the youngest of the cousins, giggled and joined in the play. The highlight of the day, however, was kept until just before they went home. Aunt Ruth had made a piñata.

"When I was in Mexico," explained Aunt Ruth, "the Mexican children just loved when they had piñatas to break."

"What's a piñata?" wondered Michelle and the other children.

"It's a hollow papier-mâché object," answered Aunt Ruth. "Like this," she said, as she showed a gaily decorated paper ball attached to a rope. "We'll hang this rope over a tree limb. Then you'll take turns being blindfolded. You will use a stick to try to hit it, but someone else will pull the rope to lift or lower it, so it is rather hard to hit."

"What happens when we hit it?" wondered Michelle.

"It will break open, and you'll all scramble to gather the candy and goodies inside. Similar to a peanut scramble," explained Grandma.

Finally the piñata was hoisted over the tree limb. Each child stood ready for action, with a sandwich bag in hand to hold the goodies that would fall within his reach. Even little Beth was expectantly waiting for a wham to break the piñata.

First one cousin tried and then another. The swish of the stick in empty air brought peals of laughter from the eager children.

Wham! There it was! Michael hit the piñata fair and square, and out poured the candy.

There were lemon drops, caramels, and lollipops. Taffy, bubble gum, and peanuts. There was a pencil. Little boxes of raisins, a toy whistle, and chocolate kisses were scattered about.

All the children scrambled to fill their bags. What fun! What giggles!

"There," noticed Michelle, "is a pack of mints." She dashed for it, just as little Beth, who had been fumbling with her bag, reached for it. But Michelle grabbed it in time, before little Beth's pudgy hands could grasp it.

Quick as a wink, Michelle realized what she had

done. And quicker still, she dropped the roll of mints into little Beth's bag.

Beth's face broke into a big smile, but Michelle's looked even happier.

Following the Golden Rule made the day great, decided Michelle. *I never would have enjoyed eating those mints myself, knowing I had grabbed them away from little Beth.*

"How was your day?" asked Mother and Daddy when they picked up the tired, but happy, twins.

"Great!" answered Michelle.

"Mine was too!" added Michael.

Then the twins took turns relating the day's happenings.

But none of the others knew about the best part of Michelle's day.

29. Great-Aunt Nettie,
Her Roommate, and Pumpkin Pie

Mildred raced from the mailbox. Dashing up the driveway, she beat the collie pup to the front porch.

"Aha! I won the race, you slowpoke," said Mildred as she reached down and patted Sparky on the head. "Now stay off the porch with your muddy paws. I'm going in to sort this mail. Today's my special day, you know."

Not only was it Mildred's birthday, but she had off from school. With Thanksgiving falling on the twenty-fifth, it meant the twenty-sixth, her birthday, was a vacation day.

Mildred was delighted. "Look, Mom! All these cards for me. One, two, three, four, five and a sixth one that must have a gift enclosed."

"It's delightful to know so many people remembered you," smiled Mother as she stacked the china plates and dishes in the cupboard. Next she cleaned the coffee percolator. Gradually the clutter on the sink counter from yesterday's company began to disappear.

"Look at this one!" squealed Mildred with delight. "Old Mrs. Townsley must have bought this one especially for me. It says, 'Happy birthday TEN YEAR OLD!' It's neat!"

"Yes, it is a cheery card. Especially since it's from her. And isn't it nice to have a friend like her that isn't exactly your age?" asked Mother.

"Yes, it sure is," agreed Mildred, as she tore open the next envelope. She was completely engrossed in the greetings, notes, and letters. The funny one from Cousin Julie made her giggle.

This was turning out to be a wonderful day—the special birthday breakfast Mother had served before Daddy and Millard left on the delivery truck, the cards, the present from Grandma Weiler, and the free time Mildred hoped to have in the afternoon to finish the craft project she had started.

"Mom, why are you doing that?" questioned Mildred as she noticed Mother putting two pieces of pumpkin pie into small containers.

"I've decided you and I should share some of these leftovers from the Thanksgiving dinner. Great-Aunt Nettie and her roommate would enjoy pumpkin pie as much as you and I do. So we'll run over to the rest home awhile this afternoon. You can feed her blind roommate and I'll feed Nettie. I'm certain they'd appreciate having us come—" Mother stopped short when she caught the sour look on Mildred's face.

"What? Spend my tenth birthday in a rest home feeding pumpkin pie to a blind lady? Sounds like a SWELL idea!" she moaned as she rolled her brown eyes about with utter displeasure.

"Oh, if you'd rather feed Great-Aunt Nettie, I don't mind. I don't care which one you feed."

"That's not the point—which one I'd feed! I just don't feel like giving up *my* vacation day. After all, it is my birthday and I wasn't anticipating spending my precious afternoon for Great-Aunt Nettie."

Mother wiped the last pastry crumbs from the sink counter, snapped the plastic covers on the pumpkin pie containers, then turned and faced Mildred's disgruntled look. She spoke quietly. "I'm surprised at your response, Mildred. Just a few moments ago you were a giggly, bubbly, happy girl. Suddenly you're changed into an angry, selfish person. Other times I thought you rather enjoyed those visits with me at the rest home."

The firm lines on Mildred's face showed that her displeasure had not lessened.

Mother continued. "It's interesting that you respond this way right after you discovered what it means to have people care about you. When other people thought of you and cared enough to let you know, you were a mighty happy girl. But right now it seems you're not willing to return the same to others. But the choice is

143

yours. You can either go over to Mrs. Weaver and take your needlepoint along or go with me. If you want to go to Mrs. Weaver's, call her and ask if it's okay to come over for an hour. If you are going with me, go change into a school dress. I'm going to get ready now." With these words Mother turned and headed for the stair door.

Mildred found herself standing alone. Angry. Perplexed. And slightly ashamed. What should she do?

The name Nettie kept ringing through her mind. It reminded her of something. But what was it? Nettie . . . Nettie . . . Nettie. . . .

Now I remember, thought Mildred. *Nettle! The vocabulary word we learned this week in school. Nettle: "to irk, to irritate." Yes, and that's exactly what's happening to me. Visiting Great Aunt Nettie nettles me. Strange, I never felt this way before. But I do today.*

Upstairs the bathroom door closed. Mother would soon be ready. An immediate decision was necessary.

"Guess I may as well go," concluded Mildred. Then she headed for her room.

On the way to the rest home silence reigned. Mother and Mildred were busy with their own thoughts.

As Mildred and Mother entered Great-Aunt Nettie and her roommate's room, fear gripped Mildred! Nettie looked sick, real sick. She didn't utter a word. But when Mildred followed Mother's example of taking hold of Great Aunt-Nettie's right hand, Mildred felt ever so slight a squeeze. But it was enough to let her know the old lady recognized her.

"Who's here?" asked the roommate.

"Mildred Martin and my mother," answered Mildred. "Remember me?"

"Yes. Did you bring something for me today again?"

asked the blind lady.

"Yes, I did," replied Mildred. "Some pumpkin pie. Shall I feed it to you now?"

While Mildred fed the blind lady, Mother stood by Nettie's bedside. Bedridden Nettie was unable to accept Mother's offer of pie. She couldn't breathe a word. At times her eyes stared, and she didn't respond to anything Mother said. Then slowly she turned her head so that she could watch Mildred feed her roommate.

"It's time for us to go, Mildred," said Mother shortly after Mildred was finished. Then she whispered, "Take Aunt Nettie's hand and say good-bye."

While Mildred held her hand, a smile lighted up Nettie's face and her lips moved distinctly, "Good-bye."

After Mildred and Mother told the blind lady goodbye and the two headed down the corridor to the exit, Mildred said, "Mother, I'm sorry and ashamed of myself— the way I reacted about Great-Aunt Nettie, her roommate, and pumpkin pie. I almost missed a birthday blessing."

Nettie's "Good-bye" was the last word anyone heard her say. That evening she slipped into unconsciousness, and one week later she passed away.

30. That Thanksgiving Essay

"Thanksgiving" was neatly printed across the top of the ruled notebook paper. The rest of the sheet was totally blank. But not more blank than Elsie Eberly's thoughts.

"It can be a poem, a story, a prayer, or even an 'I'm Thankful For . . .' listing," Mr. Anderson had instructed. "Do whatever you wish. Your papers are due on Wednesday. We'll probably be reading them orally during class."

Time had elapsed so quickly. Frustrated Elsie couldn't think of a thing to write. Basically she considered herself a thankful person. But to put it into words. . . .

It wasn't that she hadn't been searching for ideas. She'd noticed the daily newspaper had printed "The First Thanksgiving Proclamation" by George Washington. She scanned this for ideas. No success.

Maybe I could write about the courage and faith of the Pilgrim settlers, Elsie surmised, recalling her family's visit to the Plymouth Plantation. Glancing at the clock, she observed the hands telling her she had only fifteen minutes until Daddy would be home for supper. Even though Mother had so kindly excused her from meal preparation, that essay had made no progress.

"My diary of the trip—that might help!" Elsie's feet bounded up the steps, two at a time. Her catch-all drawer creaked as she opened it in search of diary, postcards, anything that would lend ideas.

Leafing through the diary, she flipped the pages to the day at Plymouth, Massachusetts. Her hastily written notes recalled, "Conditions on the *Mayflower* were almost unbearable due to disease, poor living conditions on board ship, and lack of food. Many died on the way. Of the 102 settlers that did reach America, only 50 survived till spring. Their dead were buried at night on Cole's Hill for fear the Indians would know their number was decreasing and would attack the colonists."

Elsie pondered the facts. Breathing a sigh of thanksgiving that her family had not experienced such trials, she tossed her diary back into the drawer.

Facing her sheet once more, she realized the trip upstairs hadn't really benefited her much. *My story should say something more than "I really have it good these days; we have so many blessings, I hardly know where to begin!" Why can't I come up with fresh ideas?*

Ring! Ring! Ring! The phone startled Elsie.

"Will you answer that?" called Mother from the kitchen.

"Hello, Eberlys," answered Elsie.

"Is that you, Elsie?" Mrs. Howard, the next-door widow asked. "You're just the person I'm wanting to talk to."

What does she want with me? wondered Elsie.

Mrs. Howard's request soon answered that question.

"Would you like to go with me to the Hershey Medical Center to help distribute Thanksgiving favors that I made for the children in the hospital?"

"Oh-h-h," Elsie responded. Should she or shouldn't she? "Will you just hold on a moment? I want to talk it over with Mother." Placing the receiver on the desk, she consulted Mother.

"Elsie, it's up to you. But if you can arrange to get your homework done, I'd say go along."

Elsie returned to the phone, made final arrangements with her neighbor, and within two hours she was on her way with Mrs. Howard.

At the hospital, Mrs. Howard seemed to know just where she was going. Down the yellow carpeted hallway to where the blue carpet started, then a right to the elevators, up to the fourth floor, left through the swinging doors marked PEDIATRICS, and then on to the nurses' station that was located like the hub of a wheel at the end of four hallways.

While Mrs. Howard briefly discussed the distribution

of the favors with the nurse at the desk, Elsie suddenly wished that Elsie Eberly were home writing that Thanksgiving essay. For only three feet away in a wheelchair sat the most crippled girl she had ever seen. Stealing a quick glance toward the cripple, Elsie judged her to be about her own age. And then taking a second look, Elsie was spellbound. That girl *smiled* at her! How could she?

"Come here," called the cripple in a most pleasant voice. The girls' friendship was instant.

After introducing herself as Kathy, the girl in the wheelchair said, "I heard you asking about passing out Thanksgiving favors. I'd love to be your guide."

Elsie's heart was warmed as Kathy escorted them from room to room. She knew each young patient by name and seemed to know what each one's problem was.

"This is Troy. He's only two. But he's a very sick little boy. Has no mamma or daddy. I heard somebody say he came here from a children's home."

In the next room was Alan. He was the lad who had been hurt in a bicycle accident and would possibly never walk again. Only fourteen years old.

Across the hall were two little girls. Four-year-old Cindy reached out to feel Elsie's smile. She was blind. Marguerite, the six-year-old, would probably never get inside a classroom. The doctors said she had a nerve disorder that they could not cure.

For an hour and a half Elsie, her newfound crippled friend, and Mrs. Howard chatted and cheered the young hospital patients.

"There's one more friend to see," Kathy announced. "She's in the room past the bulletin board. And then you can take a look at the bulletin board. I helped cut out colored leaves today to put on it."

The last patient was as delighted with her favor as all the other children had been.

"Now you may look at the bulletin board if you wish," said Kathy.

The bulletin board was gaily decorated with bright fall colors. With eye-catching letters the words asked, "Are YOU thankful?"

Elsie's heart was pricked. And she thought once more of her essay. The frustration of her writing assignment had vanished. Her heart was full, and she'd write till she was empty in that *THANKSGIVING* essay.

31. The Plan and That Last Spark

Fourteen-year-old Joel threw another chunk of wood on the campfire causing flickering sparks to shoot upward into the gathering darkness. The faces of the four boys glowed in the radiating firelight.

"Isn't this great?" asked thirteen-year-old Nelson as he poked another marshmallow onto his stick. White smudges on his navy sweatshirt were telltale marks that he had already enjoyed numerous toasty marshmallows.

"Sure is," replied Nelson's younger brother, Eric. "But it's good it isn't later in October. It's chilly enough," he added between munches of his relish- and ketchup-plastered hot dog.

"Yes, I was afraid we wouldn't be allowed to," said Joel. "Last week during that cold snap Dad told Paul and me we may as well give it up about sleeping out here in the woods. He knew we were counting on it ever since your parents asked if you could stay here while they're gone. But I kept hoping it would work out that we could."

"Who wants hot chocolate?" asked eleven-year-old Paul, Joel's younger brother. He poured four cups of steaming drink, passed some to the other boys, and then sipped his own. He was glad to be along on this outing with his brother and cousins although he was the youngest.

The boys snuggled close to the fire, chatted, and tittered. How cosy it was to sit around the dancing flames and watch the full moon rising behind Scrubb Hill!

"Heh! Are you sleeping already?" asked Nelson. "If so, you had better crawl into your sleeping bag and bed down in the tent."

Nelson's comments jolted Joel's thoughts back to the present chitchat.

"Oh, no! I'm not sleeping. I was staring at the campfire, and I got to thinking about the science experiment we did at school today."

"What made you think of science now?" questioned Paul.

"Oh, it was about fire. Mr. Gehman explained that fire

needs three things in order to burn."

"What are they?" wondered Eric.

"Fuel for one," guessed Nelson.

"That's right," said Joel. "The other two are oxygen and heat. Mr. Gehman also claimed a burning fire is like having the Holy Spirit."

"What do you mean?" mumbled Paul as he munched on a juicy red apple. "Explain yourself."

"I wasn't really planning to conduct a science class or a Bible lesson," stated Joel.

"You started so you may as well finish," Nelson encouraged. "Then when you're done explaining, I'm ready to hike up the hill to see if any deer came out into the clearing."

"Okay! I'm ready to go up there too. Good idea! But now about fire and the Holy Spirit . . . I'll try to say it quick-like. Mr. Gehman said you can put out a fire by taking away any of these three things. Taking the fuel away so that it dies down is like a Christian not reading his Bible or not going to church. Having a fire in an airtight place so the lack of oxygen keeps it from burning is like going places where the Holy Spirit would be choked out. And removing the heat by pouring water on a fire is quenching the flame the same as we do if we don't listen to our parents or our conscience. If we don't do what we know is right we quench the Spirit."

The other boys nodded their heads in understanding.

"Understand!" exclaimed Nelson. There was a tinge of sarcasm in his voice.

"Now what?" Paul asked. "Are we going to the clearing?"

"Yes, let's," cried Eric and Joel in unison.

After being certain the fire was burning low enough, the boys climbed the hill. They walked as silently as possible to keep from chasing any deer away. In spite of the chilly breeze, they were perspiring by the time they reached the top.

Joel flicked on the flashlight.

"Shine over there," whispered Nelson. "I see something."

"Where?"

"Over there. Give it here a minute," Nelson said as he reached for the flashlight. He shone the beam in the direction of a white mound on the other side of the pasture clearing. "What is that? It's big and white," he whispered, a bit frightened.

Joel and Paul giggled. "That's on our neighbor Brossman's property. It's an ag bag. Similar to a trench to put corn silage in."

"Never heard of anything like that before," stated Eric.

"They say the ag bags work okay. Someone said they tear easily though," Joel explained.

"Did we ever tell you about the Brossmans or the Brossmans' son?" asked Paul. "He's a pain!"

"Why?" asked Eric.

"That Barry Brossman has played more nasty tricks on us boys than I care to remember. And they always blame us for things we didn't do," Joel explained.

"I wouldn't take that," Nelson announced. "Why don't you teach them a lesson? Maybe just a little mischief on your part would cure his meanness. Have you ever tried that method?"

"No, not really . . . never thought of it that way," Joel remarked.

"Why not give it a try? Maybe even tonight," Nelson said.

"Ah . . . think we oughta do that?" Paul wondered.

154

"I don't know about that either," hesitated Eric. "You know what Mom and Dad would say."

Joel was reluctant too, but he asked, "Like do what?"

"That's easy! Looks like the ag bag is far enough away from the Brossmans' house. They wouldn't catch a glimpse of us, and yet there's enough moonlight to do our little prank. You said they tear fairly easily." Nelson glanced at each one as he continued to outline the plan. "We'll walk back and forth across the silage bag on our heels. Now and then we'll press a little harder and poke a little hole in here and there. Not often. Just enough that they get a little spoiled silage. Just enough to pay for a few of their pranks. And it's close enough to the woods that they'll think deer may have done the tearing. That's the plan."

"Well . . . I don't know . . . I'm not sure we oughta do that. But if the rest of you want to, I'm not going to be chicken," Joel said.

"Okay, boys!" Nelson spoke before Paul or Eric could state their approval or disapproval of the plan.

"Before we get involved further in the plan though, we'd better check that the campfire is completely out," advised Joel.

"Good thinking!" Nelson complimented. "Why don't you run down and put it out to the very last spark. Play it safe. Then hurry back. We'll wait here for you."

Joel nodded and jogged toward the tent. He grabbed the bucket full of spring water and headed for the still smoldering firewood. Mostly ashes were left, but here and there a clump of ashes sizzled as the water took the heat away.

Joel poured more water as he rehearsed the plan in his mind. There! He had extinguished every bit of the glowing embers. Abruptly he stopped.

"Pouring water on a fire is like quenching the Holy Spirit," the little voice inside him spoke. "Don't put out that last little spark within you."

Joel stood motionless. "I can't do it," he purposed. "I won't extinguish that last spark in my heart." Then he turned and headed up the hill to the waiting boys.

"Hey, boys, I can't do it. If we do that ag bag business I'm quenching my conscience." With that he turned back toward their campsite.

Would the others follow? Joel hoped so, but he knew he wanted to keep his spark glowing even if the others didn't. He paused. Yes, he heard footsteps following.

32. The Other Cousin

Jason was wiping the last skillet. Drying dishes didn't seem like an acceptable boy's job, but this dinner he didn't care. He knew that the sooner the dishes were done, the sooner he and Mother could go away.

Mother slipped off her apron and looked at the clock.

"Get your coat, Jason. We must be on our way. It's later than I thought."

Jason didn't know what time it was. He couldn't tell time yet. He had just turned six, not quite soon enough to go to school this term. Yes, he would have liked to go to school, but this way he got to go away with Mother or Father when one of them went away.

"Here, Mother, I got your purse for you," said Jason.

"Thank you. You are eager to get going, aren't you?" asked Mother.

Of course he was! Mother was invited to a quilting at Cousin Louise's house. And Louise, just two months younger, was Jason's cousin and best friend.

Louise *was* a girl. But that didn't matter a whole lot. Louise wasn't such a sissy girl, not like Louise's other cousin, Linda. Louise didn't scream when she saw an ant like Linda did. She wasn't giggly and silly either. Yes, Jason liked Louise, and he didn't even mind playing some girlish games, like dolls, if he could be the pretend Daddy and play with the trucks and tractors. Pretend mealtime was fun if they had raisins or pretzels to nibble on.

When Mother and Jason arrived at Louise's house, there were two other cars there.

"Looks like some of the quilters are here already," said Mother. "That's Louise's Aunt Elsie's car."

Jason didn't bother asking, "Who is Louise's Aunt Elsie?" He just hopped out of the car and headed for the door. He entered the living room where the ladies were sitting around the quilt frame. The first lady he saw was Linda's mother. So that was who Aunt Elsie was—Linda's mother! As Jason slipped off his coat, he became hopeful. *Maybe Linda isn't along. Maybe she's sick or something,* he thought. He headed for the playroom.

Sure enough. There stood Louise's other cousin, Linda! Linda was already giggling and whispering girlish-like into Louise's ear. She stopped abruptly when she heard Jason. Quick as a flash she turned toward Jason and wrinkled up her short stubby nose at him. She apparently was no happier to see him than he was to see her.

Jason was too much of a man to act as though he noticed her ugly, drawn-up face. His feet shuffled over to where the little drawing game box lay. He fumbled with the buttons. *What can I do with Linda so I have Louise to play with myself?* wondered Jason.

"Tee, hee, hee," giggled Linda. "Can't you do better than that? Tee, hee, hee! I can do it much better!"

"Here! You do it then," demanded Jason. "Then Louise and I will play together." He shoved the drawing box into her hands and headed for the truck and tractor.

"No! I want to help too!" insisted Linda.

"No!" replied Jason. He knew he wasn't doing what he should do. Neither was he speaking the way his parents taught him.

"Please, let her help too," begged Louise. "I want to play with both of you."

An idea popped into Jason's thoughts. "Okay. She may help. She will 'live' here in the playroom, and we'll 'live' in under the quilt," he explained. Although he spoke in a friendlier tone, he continued to devise a plan to escape playing with Linda.

Linda wasn't excited about that, but at least she could help this way.

Louise and Jason organized their toys and played quietly without bothering the ladies.

"I came to visit you," announced Linda's squeaky voice.

"No! Go home! We don't want visitors!" declared

159

Jason, hoping it wasn't loud enough for Mother to hear.

"You can't send me home! I'm company," replied Linda firmly.

Jason's voice rose. "Go! We're busy working!"

"Jason!" Mother's voice was stern. "Stop your fighting and get out from under the quilt." She stooped and looked at him under the quilt with a look that told him he had better do so now.

The three gathered their toys together and headed for the playroom. There they played until another idea popped into Jason's head.

"Let's play hide and seek," Jason whispered into Louise's ear. "We'll go upstairs and hide, but we won't tell Linda we're playing it. Then when she misses us, she can look for us."

"That wouldn't be very kind," Louise whispered. "I don't think we should do that."

"We'd just be surprising her," whispered Jason.

That seemed to convince Louise, so they both slipped upstairs when Linda wasn't looking.

They chose to hide behind Louise's door, peeping out now and then.

"Jason, where are you?" called Mother.

"Up here," answered Jason.

"What are you doing?" asked Mother.

Jason stammered, "Why . . . er . . . a . . . we're playing hide and seek."

"Come down here. Linda is looking for you," said Mother.

Once more Jason and Louise returned to the play-room. Jason didn't get any other ideas about how to avoid Linda, so he had to spend the rest of the afternoon sharing *his* cousin Louise and putting up with Linda's silliness.

After having refreshments, Mother and Jason left for home. Mother seemed awfully quiet and sad. She didn't talk.

"Why are you so quiet, Mother?" asked Jason.

"I'm thinking," she answered.

"About what?"

"About you, Jason."

"Why?" wondered Jason.

But Mother didn't answer his question. Instead she asked, "Which girl would you rather play with—Louise or Linda?"

"Louise, of course!" answered Jason.

"Why?" asked Mother.

"Louise is always kind. She isn't mean. She's fun to play with. But Linda . . . she does mean things! Doesn't her mother care if she's unkind?"

"Yes. I believe she does," answered Mother. "But Jason, which girl were you most like today? Linda or Louise?"

Jason thought awhile then answered, "I guess like Linda."

"Doesn't your mother care?" asked Mother.

"Of course you do!" answered Jason.

"You're right. I do care," said Mother. "I was sorry to see how you acted today, and Jesus was too."

Except for the "I'm sorry" he said to Mother, Jason was quiet the rest of the way home as he thought about how unkind he had been to Linda. His unkindness had turned the day into an unpleasant memory instead of the happy day it could have been. *Next time,* Jason decided, *I'll be kind to Linda.*

33. Little Ray in Big Harrisburg

"So high!" thought Ray, as he gazed overhead into the dome of the capitol building.

Mamma and Daddy had decided to take the family to Harrisburg, the state capital, for the day. The family

included fifteen-year-old Robert, fifth grader Ralph, third grader Ray, five-year-old Regina, and of course both parents. It was Friday after Thanksgiving, so the boys had off from school and Daddy was home from work.

When Daddy had parked the car, he announced, "It is important that we all stay together. We do not want to spoil an enjoyable day by having one of you wandering off by yourself and possibly getting lost. Now let's cross the street. The light says 'walk.'"

"Shall we go through the capitol building first?" asked Mamma. "Then we can spend as much time as we want in the William Penn Museum."

"Sounds like a good idea," said Daddy.

The boys headed up the capitol steps first. Little Regina soon saw that she had better hold on to Mamma's hand because she couldn't keep up with her brothers' pace. At the entrance of the large granite building, the three boys waited until their parents had ascended the long, steep steps.

"Hello," said a friendly voice as a stranger extended his hand toward Daddy. "You're Raymond Rissler, aren't you?"

"Yes," answered Daddy as he shook hands with the tall man in a business suit. "And you're Senator Maxwell. This is my wife, Rhoda."

"Glad to meet you," said Senator Maxwell as he shook hands with Mamma. "And these are your children, I presume," he added as he gave each of them a warm smile. "I noticed when you got out of the car that you were hometown people. Now I have a question for you, Mr. Rissler. May I have the privilege of showing you and your family my office and the senate chamber where we do the voting on laws for the state?"

"Certainly," answered Daddy. "We do not want to take up too much of your time though."

Senator Maxwell led the Rissler family through the hallways of the capitol. He explained his work. He asked the boys whether they knew who founded the state of Pennsylvania and why.

Robert and Ralph could answer most of his questions, but Ray couldn't. Actually he was more interested in not becoming lost than knowing that William Penn was the one who first settled in Pennsylvania. Ray stayed close to Mamma and Daddy. The place seemed so big and he felt so small.

Senator Maxwell continued, "This is the capitol dome. It's 272 feet from the ground."

Even little Regina was impressed as she crooked her neck and tilted her head way back to look up.

After the family had completed their tour, Daddy thanked Senator Maxwell for showing them around. Then he added, "We're thankful to have a government that allows us to worship as we please. We want to do our part in praying for you people as you make laws and enforce them. Thank you again for your time."

Daddy's words caught Ray's attention. *Pray for them?* he questioned. He couldn't imagine that. In fact he was actually a bit scared of government people, especially policemen in their black uniforms. He had never talked to any. But loving them enough to pray for them?

Next Daddy and Mamma led the way to the museum. They crossed the street and entered the round building. On the first floor were fancy glass dishes and other glassware, all made in Pennsylvania, but not many "boy" things.

But as they took escalator rides to other floors, there were more interesting things. They saw one of the first airplanes, an old milk wagon used to deliver milk door-to-door, and different kinds of old cars. As Ray became interested in the exhibits, he relaxed and forgot his fear of getting lost.

The top floor of the museum was the boys' favorite. But poor little Regina. Her short legs were quite tired by now.

"Here's a bench," said Daddy. "Why don't we sit down and rest awhile?"

"Yes, let's," answered Mamma. "My legs could use a rest too. How about you boys? Tired too?"

"Aw, I don't mind it too much. I'd rather look, than sit," stated Robert.

"May we?" asked Ralph.

"I guess it will be okay if you go over to the wildlife section. But stay together. Ray, don't you want to stay here?"

"No. May I please go along? I'm not tired and I won't get lost."

"Okay, but stay with them," warned Daddy.

On display were stuffed wild animals that could be found throughout Pennsylvania. The scenery painted behind each one made Ray feel as though he were right there in the wilds with them. There were a deer, a sly red fox, and a beaver with his broad tail.

Then Ray saw the black bear. He crossed over to get a closer look. From window to window he went, reading the display posters, absorbing as much as his third grade reading level allowed. How interesting!

"Look here, Ralph. See this!" Ray exclaimed as he pointed his finger toward a large stuffed owl. "Robert, look!"

But the boys didn't answer. Ray turned. "Ralph—" he broke off. Ralph was not there. Neither was Robert. Fear raced through Ray's chest as he glanced up and

165

down the corridor. It was filled with people, but he could not see his brothers.

Where, oh where, are they? I must have gone further than I thought.

He made his way quickly back the way he thought he had come. He turned left. Then he turned right. No boys. The more he walked, the more confused he became. He had seen this display . . . or had he?

The very thing Daddy had warned against had happened. Ray had not stayed with his brothers, and now he was lost. All alone!

Perhaps they've gone to the car looking for me, he reasoned. *There's an escalator. That's what I'll do. I'll go to the car.* Down one flight after another the escalators carried him until he saw a door marked EXIT. He pushed it open, and bright sunlight greeted him.

He walked down the sidewalk, but nothing looked familiar. Where was he? He must have come out through a different door.

Here he was—little Ray in big Harrisburg—lost! Ray could hold back the tears no longer. They came out in a rush. How long he stood there sobbing, he didn't know.

A voice behind him startled him. "Having a problem, Sonny?" The warmth of the words made him appreciate the hand laid on his shoulder.

Ray looked up. To his surprise, the kind voice was coming from a policeman!

"I'm— I'm— I'm lost," Ray finally managed.

"Well, I'm here to help you," said the policeman. "Were you with your parents?"

Ray nodded.

"Where did you last see them?"

"On the top floor of the museum," Ray said, calmer now.

"Why did you come down here?"

"I thought maybe they went to the car to look for me, but I don't know where the car is," Ray explained.

"I see," said the policeman thoughtfully. "Well, the first thing we will do is go to the information desk. Maybe your parents are there. If they aren't, we can page them."

Ray didn't know what that meant, but it sounded helpful. He took the policeman's hand as they walked back in to the main floor of the museum.

No Risslers were at the information desk, and the lady there said no one had reported a missing boy.

"What is your father's name, Sonny?" asked the policeman. "We'll page him."

"Raymond Rissler."

The policeman spoke to the lady at the desk, and suddenly Ray heard a pleasant voice announce, "Will Raymond Rissler please come to the information desk on main floor? You have a lost boy. Raymond Rissler, please come to the information desk on main floor."

The policeman smiled. "That ought to bring them." Then he added, "What's your name, Sonny?"

"Ray Rissler," Ray replied.

"Oh, you're a junior. That's nice!"

Sure enough! In a few minutes Ray saw his father's tall form walking toward the information desk. Ray ran to meet him.

"Daddy, I was lost!" Ray cried.

Daddy hugged Ray.

"He was outside, looking for your car." The policeman had walked over to where Ray and Daddy were standing, and now he smiled at Daddy. "I'm glad I found him when I did. Harrisburg is a big city."

"Oh, thank you!" Daddy said. "And God bless you. The

other two boys had just returned and told us they couldn't find Ray. We didn't know what to do, and just then I heard my name paged."

The rest of the family joined them then, and the policeman turned to leave.

After Ray explained how he had gotten separated from Ralph and Robert, Daddy said, "Children, remember I said we need to pray for government leaders? We also need to thank God for them. If it hadn't been for that policeman, we would still be looking for Ray."

Ray nodded.

"But there's something more," Daddy continued. "We told you children not to get lost, but we didn't give you instructions on what to do if that would happen. Let's sit down over here and talk about it."

Here is what Daddy told them:

IF YOU ARE LOST:

1. Pray. Ask God to help you.

2. Stay where you are. If you wander around, you are harder to find.

3. Look for someone in uniform. A policeman or a worker knows what to do to help you find your parents.

4. If you cannot find someone in uniform, and if no one finds you soon, look for an information desk. Usually it is on the main floor.

5. Do not go with strangers.

6. Do not leave the building.

34. "Three's a Crowd"

Once more Mary Beth snapped the latches of her brand-new lunch box. She had checked its contents a number of times already. "Mother, what time is it? Will the bus be here soon?"

"In about fifteen minutes," answered Mother as she

finished up the breakfast dishes. She turned toward Mary Beth. "Are you so excited about going to first grade that you think time goes slowly?"

"Oh, yes, Mother! School is going to be perfect! Diane and I can be together every day now." Mary Beth rolled her big brown eyes dreamily. "And nobody or nothing is going to spoil our fun. We'll be together all day long, day after day."

"I'm glad you're looking forward to first grade, but don't forget, Mary Beth, you're going to school to learn. And school won't be just a twosome of Mary Beth and Diane."

Mary Beth wasn't paying much attention. She was content to sit and clutch her new pencil box in one hand and her lunch box in the other. *This is going to be so neat!* she thought. *Some days we'll both take our dolls along, and the two of us will play together. Other times we'll sit and talk. Of course we'll eat lunch together . . . just like having a picnic every day.* She gazed out the window until finally the school bus arrived.

At school, Sister Wenger told the three girls and four boys in first grade to be seated at little desks. *It's just my size. I'll like to write and color here,* decided Mary Beth. *There's just one problem though. Diane isn't seated next to me. I'm sure Sister Wenger doesn't realize Diane and I are cousins and we're used to **always** being together. I'll just ask her.* "Sister Wenger, would you please move Diane to the seat beside me?"

Sister Wenger answered promptly. But Mary Beth was shocked to hear her say, "Mary Beth, in the classroom you always need to raise your hand before you speak. If you have something important to say, raise your hand. Then I will call on you to speak. And the answer to your question is no. At school we learn to be friends with everyone, not just special people." She smiled and went back to her desk.

Mary Beth fought the tears that tried to surface. First of all, she was sorry she had spoken without raising her hand. But second, and worst of all, she and Diane would not be seated side by side.

Sister Wenger didn't seem to notice Mary Beth's disappointment but continued with devotions. Next she passed out pencils, books, and paper. She explained the rules of the classroom in a cheerful but firm voice.

"Ring, ring, ring," a buzzer sounded.

"That is the recess bell," announced Sister Wenger. She gave instructions about leaving the room quietly. Then she added, "The Bible teaches us to love one another. It is important to do this at all times, even on the playground. I want all of you to play together."

Mary Beth's heart sank. *So I can't be with Diane alone even at recess time? I had hoped and planned—*

"Three's a crowd!" whispered Diane as she slowed her pace for Mary Beth to catch up.

So Diane feels the same way I do! thought Mary Beth. *Then maybe we can manage to avoid that freckle-faced girl named Sharon.*

"Diane," said Mary Beth, "tomorrow let's bring our dolls and let's not tell Sharon. That way she can't play with us."

Diane gave a nod of agreement just before Sharon joined them on the swings.

"Shall I push you?" offered Sharon, as she gave Mary Beth a hefty push. Next she gave Diane a lift before she herself sat on the third swing. In no time Sharon was swinging as high as the other girls. The girls giggled and talked while they tried to see who could swing the highest.

171

In a short time, the buzzer signaled, "Recess time is over."

The three girls brought their swings to a halt then raced toward the schoolhouse. Sharon entered first. Mary Beth slowed momentarily for Diane to catch up. "That was fun. Maybe three isn't a crowd after all," she whispered.

"No, it's not," said Diane. "Let's tell Sharon about the doll plan for tomorrow."

"Yes, let's," agreed Mary Beth. As she sat in her assigned seat, she glanced at Sharon and gave her a friendly smile.

Sharon returned the smile, and Mary Beth's heart was happy. *My first day at school is turning out great,* decided Mary Beth. *Being friends with everyone, even Sharon, is much more fun than just the two of us being together.*

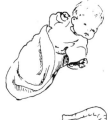

35. Blessings From A to Z

Children with names like you and me
Counted their blessings from A to Z.

A "**Acceptance**," said newly adopted **Anita**.

B **Brendon** thought, then said, "The **BIBLE** of course, and other **books** too!"

C "**Clouds**, all puffy and white, in skies of blue," stated **Carla**.

D **David** decided, "**Doctors** and **dentists** take good care of our ills and aches."

173

E "**Eyes** and **ears** that see and hear are such a blessing," emphasized **Esther**.

F **Fred**, who lived in town, thought, "**Farms** and **farmers** and the **food** they grow are so important."

G **Grace**, who looked forward to tomorrow's family gathering, smiled and said, "**Grandma** and **Grandpa!**"

H "**Houses, homes, health,** and **happiness**," listed **Henry**.

I **Inez**, who thought of her newborn little brother, quickly said, "**Infants!**"

J "**Jesus** and the **joy** He gives," was **Joel**'s ready answer.

K **Kathy** commented, "I think the **kindness** of family, friends, and neighbors is something we shouldn't take for granted."

L "**Love**," **Leon** added. "**Love** for each other and **love** for God makes this world a happy place."

M **Monica** sat up straight and tall and said, "**Mothers** . . . how precious! And Daddies too!"

N "**Natural resources** like land, forests, and mines and the things they give us," **Neil**, the reader, said.

O **Orpha**'s soft voice asked, "How could we live without **oxygen** in the air that God provides?"

P "**Preachers**, bishops, and deacons spend many hours to help us live better lives," **Peter** reminded.

Q **Queena** was ready with her answer, "**Queens**, kings, and presidents who allow people to worship God."

R "**Rain** and sunshine," was **Ryan**'s short but worthwhile answer.

S **Sarah**, glancing toward the rain-splattered window, pulled her sweater snugly about her and said, "**Shelter** from the rain and cold!"

T **Timothy** gave his teacher a friendly smile, then added, "**Teachers** to teach us to use our **talents**."

U **Una** always enjoyed family times. She said, "**Uncles**, aunts, and cousins," are an example of God's many blessings."

V **Vernon**, slowly but sincerely said, "**Vans** and buses and drivers. We'd all have to walk to school without them!"

W "**Water**. We couldn't exist without it," remarked **Wendy**.

X **Xavier** adjusted his right leg that was encased in a cast. "Without **X rays** they never would have found my problem."

Y "**Yesterdays** and the many pleasant memories they hold," mused **Yolanda**.

Z　**Zachariah**, the animal lover, decided, "**Zoo animals**, large and small, are God's creation too."

Just like these children from A to Z,
I'll count the blessings God showers on me.

36. Just a Little Piece of Gum

Charles and Christine perched themselves on the split rail fence as they waited for the school van. Here they could also watch the arrival of the employees in their father's plumbing shop.

Charles, the second grader, was first to recognize

177

employee Ben's pickup. "There comes Ben," he announced.

Fifth grader Christine challenged his statement. "Are you sure? That doesn't look like his truck."

Charles giggled as the vehicle came closer and turned into the driveway. "See, it's Ben!" exclaimed Charles.

"Okay! Okay! You're right, but you're not *always* right!" came the sisterly retort.

Ben grinned, waved, and called a cheery good morning to the children as he entered the shop. Shortly he returned, carrying pipe fittings and tools, depositing them into the company truck. The tunes he was whistling reached Charles and Christine's ears.

"Ben's always whistling and singing. I'm sure glad he works for Daddy," remarked Charles.

"Daddy is too," added Christine. "Ben's a good worker and always cheerful!"

Charles nodded in agreement.

"And I like his gum," added Christine.

"What?" asked Charles.

"His strawberry gum—he gave me some yesterday." Christine rolled her eyes and smacked her lips for added emphasis.

"How come you got some? He didn't give me any," scowled Charles.

"He gave me a piece before he went home yesterday," stated Christine with a bit of smugness.

"Where was I?" wondered Charles.

"Riding bike," answered Christine. "He opened a pack and treated me to the first piece."

Charles made a mental note of "the first piece." *So he probably has more left yet,* surmised Charles.

Brakes squeaked, announcing the arrival of the van. Charles and Christine thought no more of the activities at home, as they were soon engrossed in schoolwork.

But when Charles got home from school that afternoon, he spied Ben's truck parked by the shop. *Wonder if he has that bubble gum in the truck or in his pocket. It really isn't fair that Ben gave Christine some and none to me. He probably would have if I would have been around.* Charles glanced in all directions.

No one was around. Christine was in the house changing clothes. Mother was peeling potatoes for supper.

Think I'll just walk by Ben's truck and see if it's in there. That won't hurt, just to take a look, he decided.

There it was. On the dash—an almost full pack with the strawberry pink wrapper.

Charles's eyes scanned the area as he did some quick thinking. *Ben would want me to have a piece if he gave Christine one. Furthermore, the pack is so full, Ben would never miss just one piece of gum.*

Of course, Charles's parents had always taught him the Bible commandment *never* to steal.

This isn't really stealing. I'm just helping myself . . . to just one piece . . . one little piece, he argued within himself.

The decision was made. Quickly he tried the latch. No, Ben hadn't locked.

Charles's hand fumbled with the pack. He seized the individually wrapped, square treat, tucked it into his front pocket, and then ever so quietly closed the truck door. Away he raced to his bike, hopped on, and pedaled around to the rear of the shop.

Here, hidden from anyone's view, he unwrapped his treasure and popped it into his mouth.

After savoring the berry flavor, he tried to pop a few bubbles. *It really is as good as Christine said,* he decided, as another big bubble popped.

"Charles, Charles," called Christine. "Where are you?"

"Here," answered Charles as he pedaled around the corner. *No more bubble popping now,* he reminded himself.

"Mother wants us to rake some leaves before supper," said Christine. "And what do you have in your mouth?" challenged Christine.

"My tongue," answered Charles as he turned to get the bushel basket. *No more chewing,* he thought, *or I'm in trouble.*

Christine, busily raking, forgot to question him further.

While the children were raking, Ben came back and hopped into his own truck. He waved good-bye and was soon gone.

"Supper time," called Mother's voice.

Instantly both children raced for the kitchen door, washed their hands, then seated themselves at the table.

Daddy and Mother sat down too, and the whole family bowed their heads and thanked God for their food.

That is, everyone prayed except Charles. He had other thoughts. *What am I going to do with my gum?* he wondered.

A thought crossed his mind as Father passed the dinner rolls. While others buttered their oven-fresh rolls, Charles slid the gum into his hand and then put the wad into his pocket.

Although he was unusually quiet at the table, he soon forgot the bubble gum. Each time he saw Ben the rest of the week, however, he avoided Ben and felt pangs of guilt.

The weekend kept Ben away for a few days, and Monday morning brought school activities again.

Charles and Christine greeted Mother on Monday afternoon with their usual after-school chatter.

Then Mother startled Charles with a question. "Charles, why did you put gum into your pants pocket? I had a very difficult, sticky mess."

"I'm sorry, Mother." Charles hung his head.

"Did Ben give you some bubble gum?" Christine asked.

Charles was on the verge of saying yes, but the guilt that had been stored up for the past few days suddenly was like a flood that wanted to burst the dam in his heart.

His face burned a deep red. Slowly the story spilled from his lips. "Mother, I'm sorry," he concluded between sobs.

Just then Ben pulled into the driveway. Charles headed for the shop immediately and poured out his story to Ben. "Will you forgive me?" he asked. "I'll pay for whatever the gum cost."

"I surely will forgive you," Ben replied. "And I'm glad to see you willing to make your wrongs right. The cost of one piece of gum is so little, let's just erase that. You learned an important lesson—one little wrong can make big trouble in our lives." Then Ben gave him a pat on the arm and walked toward the shop.

Quietly Charles asked God to forgive him for stealing.

I wasn't just helping myself to a piece of gum, Charles decided. *I was stealing. I'll never do it again! Not even just one little piece of gum!*

37. The Red-Circled Day

With his smile beaming even brighter than usual, freckle-faced Fred flipped the calendar page. Although he couldn't read yet, he knew he had the right page because of the big red circle around the 11.

Big brother Thomas surveyed Fred's action with amusement, then asked, "Why are you so eager to change the calendar pad?"

"Don't you know?" asked Fred in surprise. "I thought the whole family knows what happens in November!"

Fourteen-year-old Thomas, who thrived on his younger brother's companionship, was fully aware of the circled 11. How could anyone have forgotten as often as Fred chattered about his sixth birthday? But Thomas, with a fondness for good-natured teasing, wrinkled his brow into a quizzical look. "Do you mean Thanksgiving?"

"No. Is Thanksgiving on this page too?" Fred asked.

"Sure. This red number is Thanksgiving Day," Thomas stated as he pointed to the fourth Thursday of the month.

"Thanksgiving Day is special," said Fred. "But something else will happen in November too!"

"Fred, are you thinking the last leaves will change color and drop?"

"That's not what I meant, Thomas. Guess again."

Thomas now posed a look of deep concentration. "Oh," he said, as he pretended to have finally thought of it, "the wild geese will fly south. With colder weather coming, God gives them the instinct to fly to a warmer place. Remember we see them fly in a V-shape?"

"I remember, but I was thinking something else," said Fred as he searched Thomas's face.

"Fred, what can it be?" With this he squinted his twinkling eyes into a look of complete concentration. He propped his head on his finger, pretending deep thought.

Fred could hardly keep from blurting out the answer.

Just then Thomas guessed another November happening. "I know! The whales will swim south!"

Thomas's whale comment momentarily erased all

183

thoughts of the red-circled day. Fred's eyes enlarged with wonder. "The whales? Real whales?" he questioned.

"Yes! Real whales!" answered Thomas. "My teacher saw some this summer."

"Whales just lived long ago when Jonah did!" exclaimed Fred.

"No. There are still whales around in the big oceans. My library book says there are around seventy-six different kinds of whales. And they live in many different places."

"Do they still swallow people?" Fred asked anxiously.

"No. Whales don't usually swallow people! The Bible says God had prepared a great fish, so the fish that swallowed Jonah was especially made or gotten ready to take care of Jonah. Normally whales eat fish and seaweeds."

"I see. Now, what did you say about whales in November?"

"November is usually when the whales swim south. In Massachusetts where my teacher saw some whales, it's warm in the spring, summer, and early fall. But in the late fall and winter it gets cold like it does where we live. So the whales head to a place called Dominican Republic where it's warm in the wintertime. That's hundreds of miles away. It takes weeks for them to get there."

"They can't read maps like Daddy and Mother can. How do they know how to go?" Fred wondered.

"My teacher said it's because God is taking care of them. The Bible tells us God created great whales, and He is still taking care of them. Older whales who have traveled there many times usually lead the way. Then when they arrive after their long trip, their baby calves are born."

"Calves?" questioned Fred.

"Yes, that's what baby whales are called," answered Thomas. "Here, I'll show you a picture of them in my library book. The calf swims by its mother's side until it's about one year old."

Fred studied the colored pictures in the book with great interest. "What is that smoke above them?"

"Oh, that's their breath, not smoke. They can't breathe under water, so they come to the top to breathe. They open their spout or blowhole on top of their head and let out their steam. It's like our breath on a cold day. The baby whales spout off little spouts at the same time their mothers send off big spouts. That's why you see a big and little spout side by side."

"That's cute," Fred said. "I hope I can see whales sometime."

"Perhaps someday we can."

"Thomas, how can God take care of them while He is busy taking care of everything else?"

"We can't understand, Fred. But God is everywhere all the time."

Fred didn't understand either, but it did give him a cozy feeling to know God was taking care of everything. Everything included himself. Further intrigued by the huge whales, he leafed through the book in search of more pictures.

Thomas, however, changed the subject. "Fred, we got to talking about these whales. But wasn't there something else you were wanting to tell me about November?"

Fred thought for a moment and giggled. "Oh, yes, there was! Know what's happening in November?"

Thomas grinned at his younger brother and said, "Yes, Fred. It's time for Thanksgiving. The whales are swimming, the geese are flying, and my brother is turning six. Right?"

"That's right! I knew November was a special month for me. But I didn't know it was a special time for God's nature too!" exclaimed Fred, as his finger traced the red circle on the calendar.

38. Hansel's Missing Collar

Jay searched every conceivable place, but the dog collar was seemingly nowhere. Jay was a ten-year-old who didn't give up easily, however.

He hunted behind the hedge. Beneath the picnic

table. On the porch. Down the plowed garden furrows. Around the doghouse. Beside the swing set. Along the driveway. Under Dad's workbench. Throughout the utility shed.

Now his blue eyes were searching his bedroom closet among his many collections. Probably the red collar wasn't in there either, because Hansel, his collie, wasn't a house dog. But the closet did offer one more place to look.

Fifteen minutes later, Jay plopped on the porch steps to think.

Immediately Hansel came bounding to Jay's side. This time, however, the tags that normally dangled from his collar weren't jingling.

"Sit, Hansel," said Jay, and the dog responded with perfect obedience.

"Hansel," Jay asked, "where is your collar? I looked everywhere I can think of. When you run I can't tell where you are anymore. I used to hear the tinkle, clink, clink, sound of your dog license tapping against your rabies tag. It sounded like a bell."

Hansel gave Jay's hand a responsive lick, then nestled close, resting his nose on Jay's knee.

Jay scratched behind Hansel's ear, then stroked the dog's thickening hair. "Getting your winter coat, are you?" he asked. "That's good, but I dread thinking of winter if you don't have a collar. You don't realize how serious this lost collar business is! It's law. Every dog needs a license and a rabies shot. You get a tag to wear for each one. You had both. I paid for them and the collar with my mowing money. But now they're both lost, and I have no money to replace them."

Just then Hansel snapped at a pesky bug. He zapped it, laid down his head again, then dutifully listened to his master's problem.

"This is October, Hansel," Jay continued. "And I can't get any more mowing jobs to earn money." His voice got even quieter now. "I hate to tell you this, Hansel, but if you get caught, you might be taken to the dog pound for not having a license."

Hansel turned his eyes upward to look into Jay's face. He didn't understand Jay's people talk, but he had enough dog sense to know that just now his friend needed him. Catching the frisbee or bringing back the stick were games to play when Jay felt happier. Hansel moved closer and placed both front paws on Jay's leg.

For a moment they were both as quiet as statues.

Shortly, though, Jay rumpled Hansel's fur where the collar belonged and said, "Let's go ask Mother if she has any suggestions of where to look."

They both trudged to the patio where Mother was cleaning several throw rugs.

Mother smiled. "Hello, Jay. I wondered where you were. It's such a lovely day out here. October's bright blue weather, I guess. The leaves on the sugar maple are gorgeous. Anyone feels good on a day like—" She stopped abruptly, noting Jay's doleful expression.

Jay got right to the point. "Mother, I still didn't find the dog collar. What can I do, or where can I look?"

"I don't know," said Mother slowly. "We don't take him away, so it should be here somewhere."

"No, we usually don't, except when he goes with me mowing," answered Jay.

"Did it get into the trash by mistake?"

"I hope not!" exclaimed Jay.

"I doubt it too. But you could take the garden rake and sift through the ashes on the trash pile. The collar buckle and the tags wouldn't be burned."

Immediately Jay and Hansel went to search, sifting through the ashes. But there was no trace of a dog license, a rabies tag, or a collar buckle. "At least it's not burned," sighed Jay. Then the two of them raced to the house.

"Mother, now what? There's nothing in the ashes!"

"Jay, I can't think of another place to look. But I do have a suggestion: pray about it. Remember how you wanted a puppy and you prayed for one?"

Jay did remember! He'd almost thought God wasn't going to answer. Then he had gotten several requests to mow lawn. The jobs had earned enough money to buy Hansel, plus enough to cover the cost of a rabies shot and a dog license. God had answered. And that's how Hansel had gotten his name. Mother's book of names and their meanings had said that Hansel meant "a gift from God." Hansel had been an answer to Jay's prayer.

That evening when Jay prayed he added one more petition. "And show me where to find the dog collar. Or help me earn money to replace it, if it is not against Your will."

As days slipped by, Jay continued his search when he thought of other places to look. He was curious how God was going to take care of this problem.

But when the days became a week, Jay's faith in God's ability to find the dog collar dwindled. He decided to talk to Mother again.

"Mother," he said when he found her in the kitchen, "it's a week now since I prayed about the collar. Nothing happened. God must not have heard, or He doesn't want to be bothered with my problem."

"Son, that isn't true. God does hear every prayer. But He answers them in one of three different ways. One is 'yes,' another is 'no,' and the third is 'wait.' He knows which answer is best for us. Also, never think anything is too small for Him. If He keeps count of how many hairs are on your head, He's interested in every detail of your life. Keep trusting. He'll answer. He often gives us more than we think to ask."

The ring of the phone interrupted their conversation. Mother answered, "Hello. Yes, he's right here. I'll let you speak to him." Then she handed the receiver to Jay and said, "It's for you. Bill Green, down the street, wants to speak to you."

"What does he want?" Jay whispered as he put the receiver to his ear. "Hello," he spoke into the mouthpiece.

"Jay, I was wondering if you'd help me rake my lawn on Saturday morning. You did such a good job of mowing, I'd like your help again."

"Just a moment, please," said Jay. "I'll check with Mother." He turned to Mother and asked, "Would Daddy or you care if I help Bill rake leaves Saturday forenoon?"

After a quick check on her calendar, Mother agreed to the request.

Jay assured Bill he'd be glad to help. He'd be there at eight o'clock on Saturday morning. "How nice to be helping him again!" said Jay when he hung up. "The nice part is that Hansel can go along. Bill likes dogs, and he never minded when I brought Hansel this summer."

Saturday morning dawned with autumn crispness in the air. As Jay and Hansel trotted side by side up the sidewalk, their breath spiraled into misty circles.

Upon their arrival, Bill was already at work. Jay joined right in.

"Good morning, Jay. How's this for an ideal morning to rake leaves? We won't be too warm right away. I see you have Hansel along." Then he whistled a long, low warble that beckoned the dog to his side. He playfully frisked Hansel's ears.

Soon huge leaf piles were scattered like islands across the lawn.

"I'll mulch the rhubarb and raspberry stalks with some of these leaves, and you can stuff the rest into garbage bags," said Bill.

Jay set to work filling the big bulky bags, while Bill headed for the garden with a bushel of leafy fullness.

Bill finished mulching and returned, swinging his empty basket in one hand while something else dangled in his other hand. "Jay," he called, "Hansel hasn't lost his dog collar, has he?" He continued before Jay answered, "I saw something caught on a raspberry bush. It's a dog collar with a license and some other red tag."

Jay was flabbergasted. "Yes . . . I did . . . I mean Hansel did . . . I looked . . . I . . . let me see . . . Yes! It's ours! The one I've been looking for for more than a week! Thanks!"

"You're very welcome. I'm glad it's found." Then he reached into his pocket and pulled out a five-dollar bill. "Here, Jay, take this for helping, and then you can be on your way. I can get the rest."

"Thank you!" exclaimed Jay. "You don't need to pay. Finding the collar was enough."

Bill's hearty laugh followed. Then he said, "The collar was yours and so is the money now. You earned it. Thanks for helping."

"You're very welcome," replied Jay. Then he called Hansel. As they headed down the sidewalk toward home, Jay was elated. In his right hand he clutched the dog collar, and in his left he held enough money to buy one.

His heart sang out in praise as he said, "God, thank You for answering my prayer even better than I asked. You gave me the collar and the money to buy one. You do care about little things. Amen."

Hansel looked up at Jay. He didn't understand people talk, but he knew his master looked happier than he had for a long time.

39. Three *Dozen* Oranges?

A Story From Long Ago

His thin-soled shoes, although made of leather, were
in dire need of replacement. They were not only travel

weary, but they pinched his little toes on both feet as the lad trudged home from school.

Ellis, the lad, stooped to loosen his shoe laces, but on second thought decided to remove his shoes completely. *I'll carry them to the end of Hickory Lane,* he decided. *Then I'll try to slip into them again. Ma wouldn't especially like my going without shoes in November, but she doesn't know how much they pinch. Ever since she darned these woolen socks, my shoes fit tighter than ever. My knickerbockers are getting quite snug too. But I won't complain. Ma and Pa will surely get me new clothes when they can afford them.*

Ellis now recalled the evening before. When he had supposedly been asleep in the loft, he had overheard Ma mentioning his tight shoes to Pa. Then Pa had said, "Think we can hold off till Christmas?" Ma had answered, "Well, I dunno. Ellis has been growin' like a weed lately, if you haven't noticed. But we'll try to make do till then." Pa had answered, "Before Christmas more people will be buyin' flour, 'n' I thought I could grind the extra bags of wheat 'n' sell it at the store."

Ellis's reminiscing of the bygone evening's conversation stopped abruptly as a large crow flapped its wings overhead and called out a shrill, "Caw! Caw!"

Ellis scanned the treetops, dropped his shoes and the third grade primer he was carrying, and clapped his hands with loud percussions.

A whole flock of crows flew from the treetops and across the meadow to the grove in the distant hollow.

Again Ellis's thoughts turned toward home as he retrieved his book and shoes. *I suppose Ma's busy fixin' food for Thursday's Thanksgiving dinner. Probably makin' the shellbark pie. Hope the company enjoys 'em 'cause Ma and I worked hard these evenings shellin' the nuts. 'Course it was fun listenin' to Ma's stories and sin-gin' together while we worked, but, oh, my fingers!*

By now Ellis had reached the footpath that led to the homestead. He paused briefly by the old stump to slip on his shoes, then headed to the house to see what Ma and Pa had planned for him to do after school.

Ma was busily cleaning eggs and placing them into the round willow egg basket. She smiled a greeting when Ellis said hello, but continued to count aloud so she wouldn't miscount. "Forty-three . . . forty-four . . . forty-five . . . forty-six . . . hmm, I'm three short to make it four dozen." She always included an extra egg lest one might be cracked or get broken. Then turning to Ellis she asked, "Will you please run to the henhouse and see if the chickens may have laid three more eggs?"

Ellis nodded, then carefully laid his primer on the mantel, and dashed to the henhouse. Hopefully Ma would send him to Mr. Jacoby's store with the eggs.

When he got to the henhouse, he counted, "One . . . two . . . and three!" The third egg was still warm. He hurried to the house as fast as he could without scrambling the precious eggs.

"Sure enough," Ma said. "Ellis, now I want you to take these eggs to the store. Will you be careful?"

"Yes, Ma," he promised.

Ma nodded her approval. "And," she added, "then I want you to get three oranges for me."

"Oranges?" Ellis questioned. He grew wide-eyed as he thought of such a delicacy. "We usually just get 'em at Christmas!"

Ma chuckled. "Yes, Ellis, oranges! Someone told me Mr. Jacoby has some just now. But these oranges aren't for eating as a treat. You see, I need at least three to make cranberry sauce for the turkey dinner."

"Cranberries?" asked Ellis.

"Yes, cranberries!" said Ma. "Uncle William sent me some with the folks who had gone to Philadelphia to see a doctor."

Ellis wrinkled his brow in surprise. It wasn't the first time that Ma's Uncle William, a wealthy merchant in Philadelphia, had given such an awesome gift. But cranberries, how rare and special they would be! And, of course, it was just like Ma to share her precious gift with her company.

Just then Pa came to the kitchen door. "Ellis, check with Mr. Jacoby if he's needin' more flour and if he has any empty sacks."

"I will," promised Ellis. "That's oranges and flour sacks, and I shall check if he's needin' more flour. Oh, and the eggs. Anythin' else?"

"No," answered Pa.

"That's all," added Ma.

And so Ellis left for Mr. Jacoby's General Store. Mr. Jacoby kept an account book for everyone in the neighborhood. In the book he'd jot down what each customer brought to sell and what each person bought. Then at the end of the year or in the beginning of the new year the adults would "square up," they'd say. Ellis knew that "squaring up" meant that Pa would pay hard-earned money to Mr. Jacoby if they hadn't saved back enough through the year. Or Mr. Jacoby paid Pa some money if the chickens had laid well or the crops had been especially good and they had had more to sell than they had needed to buy.

Eager to get to the store and back again before the sun set, Ellis wasted no time along the dusty path, but he was diligent in remembering not to swing the egg basket as he walked.

When he reached the porch of Jacoby's General Store, he saw the wooden crate containing oranges. Attached to the box was a sign that stated, "Oranges: thirty cents a dozen."

Thirty cents a dozen! What a hefty price! But how good they do look! They're even more tempting than a peppermint stick! he decided.

Then he entered the store.

"Can I help you?" asked Mr. Jacoby.

"Yes. I have some eggs for you. And I want some oranges for Ma. And Pa said I shall check if you need more flour and if you have any empty sacks to return."

"Fine. You have a good memory, Ellis, remembering all that without a note. No wonder your folks trust you to run errands for them. Now let's take care of the eggs first." Carefully he counted and examined them. "Good! Not one is broken!"

Ellis smiled. He was glad he was dependable, and not one of Ma's eggs was cracked.

"Now, let me check for flour sacks. Yes, here are some," said the storekeeper as he neatly folded the cloth bags and put them into the bottom of Ellis's empty basket. "Tell yer Pa I can use two more bags of flour." Then he carried the basket to the porch. "The oranges are out here. How many do you want?"

"Three," replied Ellis.

"Three oranges or three dozen?" asked Mr. Jacoby.

"A . . . a . . ." Ellis faltered. He was certain Ma meant only three. But, oh, how good they looked! Should he say three dozen?

"Three," he said again.

"Dozen?" asked Mr. Jacoby, as he raised his eyebrows with a puzzled look.

And before Ellis could muster the strength to say no,

he said, "Yes, three dozen."

Mr. Jacoby nodded, acknowledging that Ellis probably understood his mother's extravagant request. Then he counted by twos and laid the oranges on top of the flour sacks.

"Thank you kindly!" he said as he handed Ellis the orange-filled basket. "I'll write this up, and you'd better be on your way so you get home before the sun sets." He waved good-bye, then turned and entered the store.

Ellis stalked down the porch steps lugging the heavy basket. But the further he went, the heavier it seemed to become.

Thirty cents times three is ninety cents, he calculated. *Almost a whole dollar. How very expensive!* His parents never spent so much for something like oranges, not even at Christmastime.

Should he go back? No, the sun seemed to be going down fast. And yet, should he go on? What a predicament!

Just as Ellis was debating how to correct his wrong, a bad idea flashed through his thoughts. *If you walk slower, it will be dark when you get home. Then you can hide the extra oranges in the haymow. No one will know except you, and you can have a special treat every evening after school.*

Ellis's heart was now even heavier than the basket he was carrying. He didn't want to hurt Ma and Pa. But, whatever he'd do, he'd hurt them. He knew the best thing would be to tell the truth promptly, but it seemed so much easier for the present to hide the oranges.

When he reached the homestead, he noticed Ma was already lighting the kerosene lamp, and Pa was closing the doors at the horse stable.

Ellis dashed for the haymow. He dumped all but three

of the oranges in the front corner of the mow and stifled a shriek when Tabby, the cat, jumped off the haystack. Then he scattered loose hay over the pile of thirty-three oranges. Wasting no time, he raced to the porch before Pa got to the walk. He entered the kitchen.

There Ma was quietly singing "I Love to Steal Awhile Away" while she fried potatoes over the coal range for their supper. She was also frying a slab of Ellis's favorite meat, ham.

"Good! You're home!" said Ma. "I was getting a bit worried about you. I thought it took a little longer than usual. But maybe it was just that I was busy. Now wash your hands. Supper is ready and Pa's in."

Ellis set the basket on the dry sink, took the teakettle from the range, and poured hot water into a basin. He washed his hands, then seated himself at the table.

Pa also came to the kitchen, scrubbed his hands, and inquired about the flour and the flour sacks.

Ellis answered his questions, but otherwise remained silent even after they had all gathered to the table and grace was said.

Now Pa passed the bread to Ma and then to Ellis.

"No, thanks," said Ellis.

Pa gave him a questioning look, then chuckled. "You just want more room for ham and potatoes."

Soon the ham and potatoes were passed. Ellis took just a sliver of the ham and a few slices of potatoes.

"Ellis, are you sick?" questioned Ma.

"Well, yes . . . er . . . a little," answered Ellis.

"That's too bad you walked that far," said Pa, "if you're sick."

"Eat what you can," said Ma, "then go take a rest. Sure hope you don't have a flu bug right before Thanksgiving."

"Naw. I'll be all right," said Ellis as he chewed and chewed the meat fibers. Finally he said, "Mind if I don't finish my potatoes, Ma?"

"Certainly not, if you're not feeling well," she answered, concern showing in her voice.

Ellis sprawled across the wooden settee, pulled the patchwork coverlet over him, and turned his face to the wall. Warm tears washed his cheeks. He heard Ma and Pa discussing his problem in muffled tones.

After Ma had the dishes washed, she came to where Ellis was lying and laid her hand on his forehead. "Ellis," she asked, "where does it hurt?"

Ellis halted, then placed his hand on his heart. "Right here, Ma," he said.

"There?" questioned Ma, a bit puzzled.

"Yes," answered Ellis as he sat up. "Will you please light the lantern for me, Pa?"

"Yes, but why?" asked Pa.

"Please do. I want to go out to the barn and fetch something. Then I'll explain," he answered.

Promptly Pa lighted the lantern and gave it to Ellis.

Ellis bravely headed for the barn, holding the lantern in one hand and the egg basket in the other. He hung the lantern safely on a hook where the light shone dimly into the haymow. Upon his return to the house, he carefully set the basket with thirty-three oranges on the kitchen table.

Ma and Pa looked at each other in bewilderment and then at Ellis.

Ellis pulled his hankie out, wiped his tears, and then began, "I got three dozen oranges, Ma, instead of three like you told me to. I'm sorry." And then as he wept tears of sorrow, he spilled out his story.

"Son," said Pa, " 'course we're awfully sorry you did

this. But, we'll forgive you, and hopefully you'll never betray our trust again."

"I'm sorry too, that you disobeyed," said Ma. "Ninety cents is a lot of money." She picked up one of the oranges and moved it from one hand to the other. Then she wiped a tear that slid down her cheek and said, "But, Ellis, I'll forgive you too, and I'm so glad you've admitted your wrong. This year we'll just have to eat oranges for Thanksgiving instead of Christmas."

"Ellis, there's one more thing," said Pa. "I was hoping to buy new shoes for you for Christmas. But they'll have to wait till we sell more flour. I'll put new soles on your old shoes, and maybe if I put them on the shoe lathe I can stretch them a bit. It's surprising how much leather stretches sometimes."

"That's all right if they pinch a little, Pa. Each time they hurt me, I'll remember how much I hurt you and Ma. That way God can use the shoes to remind me to do what is right from now on."

Ma took Ellis's hand and gave it a squeeze. "Ellis," she said, "Pa and I love you and we've forgiven you. Remember to ask God to forgive you too. I'm sure He will. And I'm certain He'll provide for your shoes. Now, would you like to eat some supper? I'll warm some up for you."

"Please," answered Ellis, and shortly he was eating ham, potatoes, and bread.

Meanwhile, his shoes pinched his toes, but somehow Ellis knew he'd be able to tolerate them till Pa could afford to buy new ones.

40. Words and Toothpaste

Wilmer slammed the book shut without even inserting the bookmark. He stared at the linoleum squares on the floor. He didn't notice their design. He didn't notice the gleam of the fresh new coat of wax. Nor did he notice the big wax skipper his sister Mary Sue had made.

The three other Zimmerman children were playing a lively game of marbles at the kitchen table. Laughter and friendly chatter told Wilmer they were having a good time. Their merriment irritated him.

He started helping, but felt so grumpy he couldn't keep his thoughts on the game. Then Julie sent his farthest marble home. That did it!

"I'm quitting! You're just picking on me," he growled as he grabbed his marbles off the board. Although he knew it wasn't true, he added, "You're cheating and I'm not helping!" He stalked over to the recliner and grabbed his library book.

"Wilmer, what's bothering you?" asked his older brother Dale.

Wilmer wasn't about to tell. He wasn't going to let his brother or sisters know he was concerned about what was happening right now at Shady Oak School. He was fearful ever since his parents got the announcement.

The announcement read, "Notice. Parent and Teacher's Meeting at Shady Oak School. Meeting is scheduled at the school on Tuesday, January 1, at 7:00 p.m. Following the meeting, parents will have an opportunity to meet with the teachers."

Wilmer hopped off the recliner, then slumped onto the wooden rocker. He wasn't comfortable anywhere. He couldn't even concentrate while reading. Room visitation, that's what was bothering Wilmer. He felt certain he knew exactly what Mr. Rathman was discussing with Mamma and Daddy at this moment.

Mamma and Daddy had often talked with him about his problem. He had been punished. They had scolded. They had taught him what the Bible had to say about it. They had pleaded. Yes, they were fully aware he had the problem at home around his brother and sisters.

Tonight they'd hear more about the problem. Wilmer could almost hear Mr. Rathman say it. He'd clear his throat, stroke his chin, and then look directly into Daddy's blue eyes as he'd say, "Wilmer is a good student. As you noticed on his report card, he is doing well in his studies. However, he does seem to have a problem controlling his tongue. For instance, on the playground, if things don't go his way he's quick to complain or call the other children names. Later he's usually sorry about it. He doesn't seem to really mean what he has said. But he has gotten into this habit and needs to learn self-control with his speech. Perhaps you can help him at home."

The help at home troubled Wilmer. "What will be my punishment?" he muttered as he climbed the steps to his bedroom. Mamma and Daddy weren't home yet. At least he wouldn't meet up with them until morning.

Troubled sleep finally came for Wilmer. But he dreamed he heard people calling him names. He felt terrible. He awoke with a start, then realized no one was actually shouting mean things at him. When he was wider awake, he remembered last evening's meeting. He lay there thinking for almost an hour. No sleep came. His eyelids seemed heavy, and he had a headache.

Perhaps if I go to the bathroom for a drink I'll be able to sleep again, he thought. He crawled out of bed and headed for the bathroom. At the end of the hall he stopped short. *Daddy must be up already. I hear his shaver,* he thought as he turned to tiptoe back to his room.

But Daddy had seen his pajama-clad son. "Good morning, Wilmer. Come on in. I was just thinking about you," was Daddy's greeting.

Wilmer's muscles tensed. He didn't say a word, but went into the bathroom and sat on the hassock beside the hamper. He may as well get it over with. Here he could watch Daddy's face in the mirror as he shaved the grey whiskers from his red cheeks.

"I was hoping I'd get to talk with you before I leave for work. I'm glad you're up."

But Wilmer wasn't sure he was glad he was up.

"I'm glad to hear you're doing better in social studies this marking period. Your mother and I are pleased with the effort you make in your schoolwork. You are starting the year out right in that."

"Is that all Mr. Rathman had to say?" Wilmer began, half afraid to ask.

"No. Not exactly. But before we talk about the rest, I want you to do an experiment," said Daddy as he unplugged the shaver and wrapped up the cord. He walked to the closet and placed the shaver on the shelf as he talked. "Wilmer, you get that new tube of toothpaste in the medicine cabinet. Can you reach it?"

Wilmer stood on his tiptoes and stretched to get the tube on the top shelf. He held the white tube with the red and blue lettering in his hand. *What is all this about?* he wondered.

Daddy walked over to the washbowl and instructed Wilmer. "Now I want you to squeeze out five inch-long strips of toothpaste. Put them right there in the washbowl."

Wilmer wrinkled his brow and cast a questioning look toward Daddy. But he obeyed.

Soon five strips of aqua-colored toothpaste lay in the washbowl. Wilmer looked at Daddy for further direction.

"Now I want you to put that toothpaste back into the tube," stated Daddy.

"I can't do that!" exclaimed Wilmer.

"Why not?" asked Daddy.

"There's no way I can put it back in. Can I?" questioned Wilmer.

"So you think it's out of the tube for good? There is absolutely no way you can get it back in?" Daddy asked slowly as he looked soberly at Wilmer's curious face.

"No. No way. Why do you ask?" Wilmer asked impatiently.

"Because toothpaste and words are a lot alike. Once they're out, there's no way to put them back in."

Wilmer hung his head. He felt Daddy's strong arm on his shoulder. Then Daddy talked, but his voice cracked a bit as he spoke. "I know what it's like. I've had the same problem already. But what we need to do is keep from squeezing out those words we'll regret later. Are you willing to try harder, Son, with God's help?"

"Yes," was Wilmer's simple but heartfelt answer.

41. Grandpa Brown's Sidewalk Chat

Evansdale was just a dot on the New England map. Tourists driving through hardly noticed they had passed through a town. But twelve-year-old Eddie Evans thought Evansdale was the best place in the whole world.

As Eddie leaned on his snow shovel, his eyes scanned the white clapboard houses along the snow-covered brick sidewalk. The houses seemed to be as closely related as many of the residents were. The design of each neat home varied only in the color of paint on the doors, shutters, and trim around the dormer windows.

Maybe I'm a wee bit partial because Evansdale is named for my great-grandfather, Eddie decided. *Everyone always speaks well of him. I'm privileged to be one of his descendants. Anyway I've never lived anywhere else, and hopefully I never will.*

"Toot! Toot, toot, toot!" beeped a passing van, jolting Eddie from his daydream.

Everyone knew everyone else in Evansdale. Obviously, the van driver was amused to see Eddie jump from his reverie on the shovel prop. Eddie grinned back, and his hand waved a greeting.

Then he chuckled to himself. *Never knew a horn could scare me that much! Guess I was loafing on the job.*

But as he set to work, his smile vanished, and a frown took its place.

He looked at the section of drifted sidewalk still to be cleared. The next-door neighbors had already cleared their portion.

Not half done! he exclaimed mentally. *I was just thinking how nice Evansdale is. I like most everything and everybody here, but I don't like the unwritten law about cleaning sidewalks.*

Once more he thrust the shovel into the drift. But he loaded it too full, and half of the snow toppled onto the walk again. He backed up and sighed. Then he propped himself on the shovel handle once more. *Why can't Evansdale get a maintenance man like the school has? Why must each household clean its own sidewalk? And I,*

Eddie Evans, automatically get the job in our family! And ev-e-ry time this old sidewalk needs shoveling, there's skating or tobogganing.

Eddie's boot kicked at a twig half hidden in the drift.

Furthermore, the caretaker, custodian, or whatever we'd call him could replace the broken bricks. Then in the fall he'd clear all the maple lea—.

"Thinking hard?" a voice interrupted.

Startled from his prop the second time, Eddie turned to face Grandpa Brown. "Well, er . . . a . . . yes. Guess I was," he stammered. "Resting too," he added.

Grandpa Brown wasn't a flesh-and-blood relative to any of the other Evansdalers. Tragedy had claimed his family many years ago. But the bitter experience had served only to make him more kind and sympathetic. Everyone in town loved him, and because he was the town's oldest resident, townsfolk affectionately called him Grandpa Brown.

"Sounds like a healthy diet for a young man," quipped Grandpa Brown as he good-naturedly tapped Eddie with his cane. "Some good hard work, seasoned with a little rest and sprinkled with much thought, makes your age or mine thrive."

As always, Eddie was glad to chat with Grandpa Brown. Furthermore, it gave him a legitimate excuse not to shovel for awhile.

"So you're out for a walk?" asked Eddie.

"Yes, I'm walkin' to the grocer to get bread 'n' milk. Thanks for cleanin' the sidewalk. It helps a young fellow like me stay right side up," chuckled Grandpa Brown.

"Oh?" replied Eddie, and he felt slightly guilty. *If he'd only know how I feel!* he thought.

Grandpa Brown didn't seem to notice Eddie's embarrassment. "Evansdalers have always done their part for

210

others' benefits," said Grandpa Brown. He adjusted his spectacles and then continued, "Remember yo' great-grandpa? Or had he died before you were born?"

"Yes and no," answered Eddie. "Yes, he died before I was born, so no, I don't remember him. Tell me about him."

"Interestin' you ask 'bout him. I was just thinkin' 'bout him when I saw you clearin' the sidewalk. He would've been glad to see his great-grandson doin' his job without complainin'," said Grandpa Brown.

Eddie shifted from one foot to another and chided himself. *I don't deserve that!*

The old man continued, "I was in my youth when I heard him preach his 'Sidewalk Sermon.' He said, 'If we each sweep our own sidewalk, the whole town will be clean. And the same is true in the church. If we each sweep sin away at our door, the whole church will be clean.' A powerful sermon! One I'll ne'er forget. I've been tryin' to practice it ever since." He pulled a red hanky from his pocket and dabbed at a tear that was sliding down his wrinkled cheek.

Eddie was listening carefully. *That's what makes Grandpa Brown so special!* he decided.

"So Eddie," added Grandpa Brown, "keep on faithfully doin' yo' part in cleanin' life's sidewalks. Now I must be on my way," he said. Then he shuffled on up the sidewalk. His patched galoshes and cane left unique imprints in the remaining drifts.

Eddie watched until Grandpa Brown was out of sight. Then he grabbed the shovel and set to work. *Enough poking! This sidewalk is going to get cleared in short order. What a bad attitude I've had toward an important job!*

Eddie swung shovelful after shovelful, erasing Grandpa

Brown's footprints in the snow.

At the moment, he could not see the permanent imprint Grandpa Brown's chat had left on him, however.

Two days later Eddie learned that Grandpa Brown had passed away. That day on the sidewalk they had had their last chat.

I'm glad Grandpa Brown told me about that sermon, he thought. *Like him, I want to keep my sidewalks cleared.*

42. Keeping the Woodbox Filled

"Nathan, will you please bring in another load of firewood?" called Mother.

Nathan was tempted to ignore the call.

"Didn't I hear Mother call?" questioned Daddy, as he stopped the electric drill.

"Yes, I guess she did," answered twelve-year-old Nathan as he headed for the shop door.

"Nathan! Nathan!" Mother continued to call.

"Yes," answered Nathan.

"Will you please bring in more firewood?" Mother requested.

"Okay," he growled. Then he got started with the dreaded job. Chunk after chunk of wood was heaped on the express wagon. Nathan inserted long sticks vertically as sideboards to help hold the load together. At last the wagon would hold no more.

Nathan was strong for his age, but all his muscle power was needed to get the wagon going. He pulled and tugged.

At last, the load began moving. But as the wheels rolled on the bumpy ground, first one, then another and another piece of firewood tumbled to the ground.

Nathan was disgusted. *I like sitting by the crackling fire on a cold winter evening,* he thought. *But I sure do hate keeping the woodbox filled.*

Kerplunk, clunk! He tossed the wood pieces back on the wagon. One hung precariously close to the edge then dropped to the ground again.

Eventually Nathan had the woodbox filled, the floor swept clean of wood chips, and the wagon back in place. Finally he was back at Daddy's side and watching.

Daddy glanced at Nathan and smiled.

Nathan wore the same somber look he wore while filling the woodbox. He hated that chore.

"Why so glum?" asked Daddy.

Nathan was quick to answer, "I hate filling the woodbox! And it's always my job."

For a moment Daddy didn't say anything. He continued shaping the metal he held. Then he laid it on the workbench and turned toward Nathan. "Why, Nathan, I'm surprised you're fretting about doing something important like filling the woodbox."

"Important?" questioned Nathan.

"Yes, important," answered Daddy. "It's like working in cooperation with God."

Nathan's eyes widened. "What do you mean?"

Daddy continued, "God knew we would need heat to keep our bodies warm. To have heat, we need fuel. So God made provisions for us when He formed the earth. He put coal and petroleum deep under the surface of the earth. He caused the trees to grow for our use."

This was a new thought to Nathan. "You mean God planned that we burn firewood? It doesn't seem like God would be interested in a little detail like firewood," said Nathan.

"Being warm is not a little matter. If we wouldn't have heat, we'd freeze. This is just another way that shows God cares for His people."

Nathan thought for awhile, and then he asked, "Are wood, oil, and coal the only ways to heat homes?"

"No, some people use electricity to heat their homes too," said Daddy.

"Then God didn't prepare for that, did He?" Nathan asked.

"Think," said Daddy. "How do we get electricity?"

Nathan answered quickly. "Power plants generate it."

"How do power plants generate it?" asked Daddy.

"I guess with water."

"Who made the water?"

"God," answered Nathan.

"That's right. Man can make inventions, but we still depend on God and His provisions for our inventions to work. Some power plants use atomic power to generate electricity," said Daddy.

"How does that work?" wondered Nathan.

"It is a very complicated process," Daddy began, "but atomic energy is produced by splitting tiny elements called atoms. When atoms are split, they give off tremendous light and heat, which is then used to generate electricity. Unfortunately, atomic energy has been used very destructively too. As Christians, we must always use God's resources wisely."

"Guess we should be thankful for them too," said Nathan.

"That's right, Son," agreed Daddy. "When we pray and thank God for our nice warm homes, we really should mean it from our heart. God is taking care of us in ways we hardly think of. Too often we take His care for granted."

Nathan nodded and then chuckled. "So what you're saying is that keeping the woodbox filled is a privilege instead of a chore? Okay! I got the message."

"And I have one further suggestion," said Daddy. "Maybe you could try to keep it filled without Mother always needing to tell you to."

Nathan smiled at Daddy and thought, *Guess Daddy and Mother are two more of God's provisions I take for granted. God really did plan for my good. Maybe I should go see if I can get another load of wood into the box.*

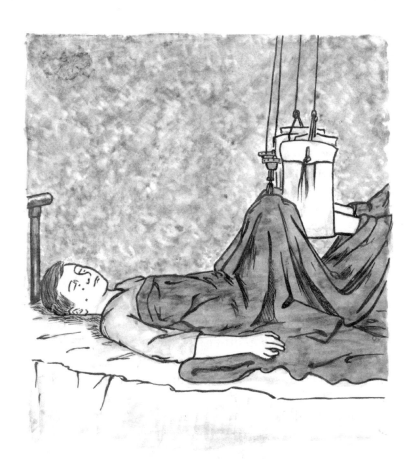

43. Roy's Useless Days

Roy turned to his side as best he could. He wanted to find a more comfortable position. But that wasn't possible. *How can I take this?* he wondered. *Six weeks in traction? A cast to my waist! How can I?*

No one answered his question for he was alone. Alone in Room 304 at the local hospital.

Mother had been in awhile in the afternoon. But now she was home preparing supper for the others. Dad and Roy's brothers and oldest sister would be coming in the evening. These hours alone went so slowly.

I often secretly wished I wouldn't have to feed the calves and help with the chores after school, thought Roy. *Now I wish I could be doing that! I'm not only lonely here, but **useless** as well!*

Six weeks seemed ever so long to twelve-year-old Roy. Normally a healthy lad, his life had changed ever so quickly. Ever since the auto accident his family was involved in, he, active Roy, had been an invalid.

Why me? he questioned. *The others had only a few scratches and bruises. I'm glad they weren't hurt more. But why did I have to be?*

Answers to his questions didn't come, but big salty tears did. One after another slid down his cheeks.

"Roy," a soft voice called, "are you sleeping?"

Roy whisked the tears from his cheeks and turned to greet the visitor.

There stood Floyd Martin, one of Roy's favorite people. Floyd, a minister from church, was also a neighbor and a friend of Roy's family. Kindness and understanding seemed natural for Floyd, making him a fine example of cheerfulness.

Floyd laid a hand on Roy's shoulder. "Roy, are you feeling up to having company?" asked Floyd.

"Er . . . a . . . yes," answered Roy as he brushed his hand across his cheeks to dry any lingering tears.

"I know what it's like to be in the hospital, Roy," said Floyd. "I've been in myself ten times."

Ten times! thought Roy. He hadn't known that. He always thought of Floyd as being part of the bright side of life.

"Have any pain?" Floyd asked.

"Well, no, not really. The first couple of days I did. But no pain now. I'm just uncomfortable with my legs up like this," answered Roy.

Floyd nodded. "These uncomfortable days can be just as trying as pain-filled days," he agreed. "We have more time to think, time to pity ourselves, time to become bitter that God allowed such a thing to happen."

Roy was amazed. *Did Floyd get those feelings too, sometimes?* he wondered.

"Different times I'd get discouraged and feel so alone, so useless, when I was ill. Others were up and about doing things and there I was in bed," Floyd was saying.

Did he see my tears? wondered Roy. *He seems to know exactly how I feel.*

Floyd continued. "One of those times when I was ill I got to read about a lady who felt the same way I did. She was an invalid for almost fifty years."

"Fifty years!" exclaimed Roy. "No wonder she felt useless! Six weeks is bad enough!"

Floyd smiled. "That's right! At the age of thirty-three she became ill, and she lived till she was in her eighties. She used to be a busy lady who liked to draw and write humorous verse. Then she became sick. Sick and bitter. She was unhappy and made all those around her unhappy."

Roy listened. This was interesting. The lady must have felt a lot like he did. *No wonder she was feeling blue,* thought Roy. "Who was she?" he asked.

"Charlotte Elliott," answered Floyd. "The lady who wrote the song, 'Just as I Am.' Do you know that song?"

"Yes," said Roy. "When our class at school sings at the rest home, people often select that song."

"Yes," continued Floyd. "That hymn has spoken to the

219

hearts of many people. In fact, during Charlotte's life she received letters from a thousand people telling her what that song meant to them."

"It's a wonder she felt like singing, much less writing a song, if she was in bed."

"That's right," answered Floyd. "But a change in her heart made the difference. One night she was especially blue. She was home on the sofa as usual. But her family was away. She was alone and feeling totally useless. The rest of her family were helping to get ready for a sale, similar to a garage sale. The sale was to help raise money to start a school for poor girls to attend. How she wished she could help too! That night she hardly slept. The next day her family went to the sale. Again she was alone and depressed. Then she thought of an incident in her life fourteen years before."

"What was that?" asked Roy.

"Charlotte's family had a dinner guest that evening. It was a minister Charlotte's father knew. Dr. Cesar Malan was his name. He was well-known because he wrote hymns. That night Charlotte was her unhappy self. While guest and family were seated around the table, Charlotte burst out in anger. She condemned God, saying He was cruel to her for allowing her to be sick. She criticized her father, her brother, and her sister and said they had no sympathy for her."

"At the table? In front of company?" questioned Roy.

"Yes," answered Floyd. "Her father, her brother, and her sister each excused themselves and left the table. They were so embarrassed."

"I guess!" said Roy. "What happened then?"

"Dr. Malan and Charlotte sat facing each other for awhile, neither saying a word. Then he said, 'You're tired of yourself, aren't you?' 'What do you mean?' she questioned angrily. He explained that she had hate and anger because she didn't have anything else to cling to."

"What happened then?" wondered Roy.

"Charlotte realized Dr. Malan understood her and was trying to help. She apologized for how she had acted at dinner for now she was embarrassed.

"Then she asked how to go about being a different person. 'Give yourself to God just as you are now, with your fightings and fears, hates and loves, jealousies and quick temper, pride and shame . . . and He will put love in their place.' Charlotte did just that. But, as all of us need to do, she had to accept it again and again when things came along that weren't exactly the way she would have liked them to be. Fourteen years later then at the time of the sale, she was still an invalid. Once more she remembered Dr. Malan's words, 'Come just as you are.' She took her pen and wrote the poem, 'Just as I Am.' This helped her feel better, but at the time she didn't realize how much those words would mean to others."

Roy smiled. He had forgotten all about his own problem. "What she did was probably worth more than what the others did who weren't sick," he said.

"Yes! Charlotte's brother said, 'In all my preaching I have not done as much good as my sister has been permitted to accomplish by her one hymn.' Charlotte's grandfather, father, uncles, and brother were all ministers. But God used her too, even though she was sick for most of her life. She felt alone and useless. But God used her for good, just as He'll help us to be kind, helpful, and loving while we're laid up for a while."

"Excuse me. Here's your supper," interrupted a nurse.

Floyd glanced at the clock. "Is it that time already?" he remarked.

"That's okay," said Roy. "I'm glad you took the time to

tell me about Charlotte. I was feeling rather blue before you came. This will help me."

During a short time of prayer, Floyd asked God to help Roy to be patient during this seemingly useless time. He asked that this could become an especially useful time, a time that Roy would grow like Jesus' example in favor with God and man; also that healing might be on the way if it was His will.

"Good-bye now," said Floyd as he waved and disappeared down the hallway.

Roy turned, as well as he could, toward his supper tray. Life somehow didn't seem as glum anymore. *I'll be as patient as I can. It will help me and maybe others too. Then these six weeks won't be useless days after all.*

44. "This Is the Day"

"Mary Sue, time to get up," called Mother. "Are you awake?"

Mary Sue only managed to grunt an answer. She could already tell it wasn't going to be her kind of day. It was raining! Her skating plans were all spoiled!

Guess I'll just stay in bed, thought Mary Sue. *What a day for a vacation! I was planning all week to go skating with Marcia. She was going to bring her brand-new skates. I planned to wear Beth's.*

Beth, Mary Sue's sister, had outgrown her size six skates. Her skates needed only to be sharpened. Then they'd be ready for Mary Sue to glide in.

Mary Sue finally dragged herself downstairs after slipping on her green knit dress. She shivered uncomfortably. Rain pelted against the windowpane, and the sash rattled from the windy gusts.

Mary Sue tugged at her sleeves. Even the smell of bacon and eggs frying didn't please her. She pouted from head to toe.

Beth was exactly the opposite. Changes in plans or weather didn't seem to affect her. Now she was interested in the new calendars they were going to hang up. A smile danced across her face, and her voice was as cheery as springtime's first robin. "Isn't this a neat picture?"

"Where is that?" asked Jerry, Mary Sue's younger brother. He was in second grade and was just beginning to learn of new places and things.

"It doesn't say," replied Beth. "Looks like Florida though. Maybe it's close to Uncle Pete's."

Now they heard Daddy coming in from doing the chores. He took off his wraps and washed his hands and face.

The family gathered to the table to enjoy the breakfast Mother had prepared.

"Smells good. A good breakfast to start out a good day," said Daddy.

"And a good year, I hope," Mother added.

They all bowed their heads for silent grace. Then the

224

family conversation continued. Each one said what he hoped to do this New Year's Day. Friendly chattering mixed with the clatter of silverware.

Everyone's, that is, except Mary Sue's. *How can they be so happy?* she sulked. *Even the bacon is fried too hard. And, ugh—there's oatmeal. Who's hungry for oatmeal?* Mary Sue looked as sour on the outside as she felt on the inside. She didn't care. *It's raining and the skating's ruined. . . .*

"Deep in thought?" Daddy questioned, interrupting her thinking. He was looking directly at her. "Did your smile turn somersaults and not end with the right side up? Or did you forget to put it on this morning?"

The rest of the family giggled at Daddy's questions. Mary Sue didn't. He wasn't one bit funny. In fact, she felt more sorry for herself now than she had before. They just didn't understand her. They had no idea how much she had looked forward to a day of skating with Marcia. Such a way to begin the New Year!

"It's disgusting!" she finally blurted. "Rain the very day I planned to go skating with Marcia. Tomorrow we go back to school. When can we skate now? Why did it have to get warmer? Why not colder?" The anger spilled out as she continued to gripe and complain.

After Mary Sue's outburst, silence reigned. Daddy cleared his throat. Mary Sue stirred and stirred her oatmeal. She didn't eat. The lump in her throat was growing. *How much better it would feel to cry, than to try to eat this horrible oatmeal,* she thought.

Finally, Daddy spoke. "Mary Sue, haven't you learned yet that we don't control the weather?" He paused, then continued, "So . . . it's raining. But are you going to allow that to ruin your day?" His words became firmer now. "You have a habit of getting upset when things

225

don't go your way. As Christians we have no right to condemn the weather. God sends the sunshine, rain, heat, and cold. He controls it. Who are we to complain about His perfect planning?"

Mary Sue didn't answer.

"Now eat your cereal," continued Daddy. "Then if Mother doesn't care, you may ride along with me to town. You can walk over to Binkley's and get your skates sharpened while I'm at the mill. Then your skates will be ready to go when the pond freezes."

Mary Sue's frown began to melt away. The lump in her throat began to dissolve. She thoroughly enjoyed going to Binkley's sharpening shop.

Mr. Binkley, the owner, was a cheerful person. Everyone liked him. He had lost his family and his right leg in an automobile accident several years before. But rather than feeling sorry for himself, he spread cheer to everyone who stopped in.

Within an hour of Mary Sue's outburst at the breakfast table she was opening the door to Binkley's shop. Singing greeted her ears. *Sounds as happy as ever,* she thought as she stepped inside. Mr. Binkley didn't hear her enter. He continued to work. Sometimes he sang, and the next moment he whistled a tune. What was he singing?

Mary Sue stood quietly. She listened and thought. *How can he be so cheerful?* Just then she recognized the familiar song he sang.

This is the day that the Lord hath made;
We will rejoice and be glad in it.

Mr. Binkley finished singing.

"Oh, good morning, Mary Sue!" was his warm and friendly greeting when he saw her. "I didn't know anyone was here. What can I do for you, young lady?"

"Oh, . . . a . . . why . . . a . . . ," she stammered. She couldn't even think what she wanted here. "Oh, pardon me, I was thinking something else," she finally managed. "I'd like to have these skates sharpened."

After he took the skates, she pulled the heavy door open and dashed out into the rain. She turned her eyes toward the dark skies overhead. *No sunshine in sight, but I will rejoice and be glad anyway. Because this is the day the Lord has made!*

When Mary Sue reached Daddy's pickup, he was waiting on her. One glance at her smiling face told him her attitude had improved. Somehow he didn't feel it necessary to tell her he had more than one reason for bringing her to Binkley's that day.

45. Preacher's Children

The note said: "Went to Irwin Miller's. Child was hurt in a car accident. Get supper ready and clean living room, Rosalyn. Andrew, get milkers ready and feed heifers. Love, Mom." It lay silently on the table until the school van drove in.

At 3:20 p.m. there was a thud against the back door. Then it burst wide open. "Beat you in this time!" eight-year-old Andrew Martin shouted.

Andrew and Rosalyn both scrambled to get into the kitchen first. But everything was silent. Mother and little James weren't around. The scholars plopped their books and lunch boxes on the counter.

Rosalyn, the sixth grader, spied the note just as Andrew did. She dashed to the table and tried to grab the message first. But he already had it.

"What does it say?" asked Rosalyn impatiently.

"Went to Irwin Miller's. Child was hurt in a car accident. Get supper ready and clean living room, Rosalyn. Andrew, get milkers ready and feed heifers. Love, Mom," he read.

For a moment neither of them said anything.

"They're gone again!" Andrew reacted.

"Yes! Guess we ought to feel sorry for the Millers. Well, I do . . . but it seems whenever anything happens to anyone else, *we* always have to suffer too," Rosalyn thought aloud.

"It wasn't this way before Daddy was ordained to be a preacher," Andrew added. "They didn't go away half as often then."

"Well, he can't help that," Rosalyn reminded.

"I know. I know!" replied Andrew. "But it *is* true we have to share our parents with everyone else. Isn't it?"

"Yes. It's true. They have so little time. Little time to spend just for fun things with us. There's always someone sick to visit or old people to see."

Andrew added to the list. "And weddings . . . and funerals. . . ."

"Or people with problems coming here at any time. Guess we ought to hang out a 'Visiting Hours' sign like

229

Dr. Matthews," smiled Rosalyn.

"Not only that!" Andrew continued. "We get loaded down with extra work. I get tired of it. Scott Anslow and Michael Burton don't have to work. They'd learn if their daddy were a minister. They get off easy. Never have any chores."

By now Rosalyn was munching on the apple slices she had spread with peanut butter. But the delightful taste of juicy apple blended with the peanut butter flavor didn't register with her taste buds. She was too busy thinking of all the bad points about having her father ordained to the ministry.

"We don't just have it tough at home," she mused aloud. "Everywhere I go people watch me. Then they ask, 'Does the preacher's daughter act *that* way?' " mimicked Rosalyn.

"That's for sure!" agreed Andrew. He remembered a few too many times when he hadn't shown his best manners and conduct. And he remembered how others had noticed.

The clock interrupted. The chimes announced four o'clock had already arrived.

"Andrew, four o'clock! We've got to get a move on! We'll never be done in time if we don't hurry. And I had hoped to work on that decoupage motto for Mom." She busied herself putting their books, lunch boxes, and wraps in order.

"That's right! This is Friday, and Tuesday is Christmas. We'd better hurry. I'm not done with Daddy's footstool either. Maybe Saturday we can do it. They're going to Dave and Kathy's wedding, remember?" he asked. After changing his clothes, he headed for the barn. Once busy with chores, he forgot about the "preacher's children" conversation they had had. He pulled his beanie down over his ears further. It felt like snow in the air.

Rosalyn also felt like her cheery self by the time the family gathered to the supper table. For the present she dismissed the woes of being a minister's daughter.

Saturday arrived, cold and blustery. Again Mom and Daddy were gone. Little James stayed home with Rosalyn and Andrew as he usually did when they weren't in school. The two oldest children hustled through the day's work. Then they began working on the finishing touches for the Christmas gifts.

Excitement filled the air. Rosalyn and Andrew chatted and laughed as they worked. Baby James, happy after his nap, prattled away with baby talk. He played with the scraps of wood beside the workbench.

"What was that?" Rosalyn wondered as she heard a sudden bump.

"Someone's at the—"

Andrew never finished saying "door." Scott Anslow and Michael Burton, the two neighbor boys, came bounding in.

"What's that?" asked Scott abruptly.

"A footstool. Daddy's Christmas gift," replied Andrew.

"Ha! I'd never make anything for my pappy. He couldn't care less about me. So why should I make somethin' for him?"

Michael was inspecting Rosalyn's project. "You makin' somethin' too? What is it?"

"A motto. Our Christmas present for Mom," Rosalyn answered.

"What's it say?" Michael questioned.

Rosalyn turned the motto so Michael could read it.

"Praise ye the Lord! Oh, whew! What does that mean? Praise the Lord for what?" Michael asked with emphasis.

"Oh Michael, there are lots of things!" Rosalyn responded. "God gives us gifts every day!"

Scott interrupted, "My mom's so busy decorating every room in the house. She told us younguns to get lost until she's done trimming the tree. I hate Christmas. Oh, the gifts I get are all right. But my folks are always shopping and yet fussin' 'bout how much money it takes."

"My folks are never home!" Michael grumbled. "Office parties . . . club parties . . . they're going out tonight again. Gettin' a baby sitter for us. I'm glad when this Christmas stuff is over. The other day I saw a sign that said, 'Peace on Earth—Goodwill Towards Men.' Huh! At our house it's just the opposite at holiday time!"

Just as suddenly as they came, the neighbor boys departed. The workshop remained very quiet.

Rosalyn finally broke the silence. "What do you say? We don't have it so tough after all being preacher's children, do we?" She scooped up Baby James into her arms and hugged him tightly. "Our family knows what 'Peace on Earth—Goodwill Towards Men' means, don't we?" she asked as she planted a kiss on her baby brother's dimpled cheek.

"And know what? With Daddy being a minister, perhaps more people can find out what it means," Andrew replied.

46. This Little Light of Mine

The last notes of "This Little Light of Mine" faded as Paula turned to the open suitcase before her. *Just two more days till Christmas vacation,* thought Paula. *And then. . . .* Her thoughts went on and on of what this year's Christmas vacation would include.

The trip . . . the long-awaited, wished-for, and talked-about trip to New York was just two days away! There was going to be time with Grandpa and Grandma. There would be play and talk time with Paula's almost-twin cousin, thirteen-year-old Lynette. The traveling time all the way from southern Georgia to upstate New York would be such a special time for family togetherness. They'd watch the scenery, sing, and play games.

"Paula," called Mother. "Are you getting your suitcase packed?"

"Getting there," answered Paula, as she folded her seldom-used flannel nightie. *Better pack this one,* she thought. *Just maybe we'll get to go to bed during a northern snowstorm. Wouldn't that be great?*

Philip rapped on Paula's half-open bedroom door. "Aren't you done yet?" he questioned. "Mine is all packed, and Mother checked and okayed it."

Paula turned to her eight-year-old brother. "Almost," she answered and smiled. "Won't this trip be great?" She knew Philip was anticipating the trip with as much eagerness as she was.

Philip's eyes beamed. "Yes! It will be great! And know what Mother told me?"

"What?" Paula asked.

"We'll pack one lunch to eat in the car along the way, and the other meals we'll eat in restaurants. And we'll sleep at a motel."

"Really?" Paula's eyes lit up. "I thought we'd have picnics like we do other times." She didn't comment about the motel because she had been aware of that.

"No. It's too cold up north for picnics this time of the year! Usually we travel in summer."

Pitter-patter footsteps sounded from four-year-old Priscilla's room. She was awake from her afternoon nap.

Paula swooped Priscilla into her arms and gave her a hug. "Now you just have to sleep two more nights and one afternoon nap. Then we'll go far away on our trip," Paula told her.

Priscilla giggled and nodded her head. She sensed Paula and Philip's excitement.

The hustle and bustle of trip preparation made the next two days pass quickly.

Finally the morning arrived, and they were off.

Just like Paula had imagined, they played games, watched scenery, talked, and laughed. The packed meal was delicious and allowed them to keep driving. Then the stop at the restaurant that evening was just what they needed—hot food and a nice break from riding in the car.

And the motel! It even had a kitchenette. Priscilla raced around trying to look at everything at once. Finally, Daddy made her sit quietly in a chair until she calmed down.

The next morning, Daddy and Philip carried the luggage to the car while Mother combed Paula and Priscilla.

Paula washed Priscilla's face following the good breakfast they ate in the kitchenette.

"All aboard," Daddy called, as everyone scampered to the loaded car. He checked his watch and predicted, "We'll probably be around Scranton, Pennsylvania, by lunchtime."

"Any good restaurants there?" Paula piped up.

"Why? Does that concern you? You surely aren't hungry now, are you?" teased Daddy as he looked at Paula in the rearview mirror.

"No, but I'm trying to decide now already what I'd like to order," answered Paula.

"Maybe you're looking forward to it, but I'm not,"

stated Philip in no uncertain terms.

"Why not?" questioned Mother. Philip was usually the hungry one.

Philip's face flushed. He wished he would have kept his mouth shut.

Daddy, once more glancing in the rearview mirror, asked, "Care to explain?"

"Because I don't like to pray in public," Philip blurted out. "I know God gives us our food and I do want to thank Him for it, but not at a restaurant!"

Daddy thought, then cleared his throat. Finally he spoke. "What makes the difference there, Son?"

"I feel everyone watches us. Others don't pray," answered Philip. "And," he continued, "with the twinkly Christmas lights blinking I can't concentrate. Besides there is a whole line of people in a hurry, waiting to be seated at tables. Should we take the time and make them wait longer to use our table?"

Paula stared at Philip. *This sure doesn't seem like my brother Philip,* she thought. *But I have a problem myself with not being able to concentrate.*

"Did you know, Philip, that Jesus thanked God for food once in front of 5,000 people?" Daddy asked.

"Was that the time He fed them with the five loaves and two fishes?" Paula asked.

"Yes," said Daddy.

"But those people loved God, didn't they?" Philip asked. "Last evening I saw some boys looking at us when we prayed. Then they laughed."

"Ah," said Daddy. "So it's not so much that you don't want people to have to wait on us—you don't like to stick out like a sore thumb."

"I guess so," Philip admitted.

"Well, let's think about meals, Son. Where, really,

does our food come from?"

"From God," Priscilla chimed in.

"That's right," said Daddy. "Philip, if someone had come up to us last evening and told us he was going to pay for our meal, we surely would have said thank you, wouldn't we have?"

"Sure," Philip replied. "It would have been impolite not to."

"And we wouldn't have hesitated because of others watching us, would we have?" Daddy asked further.

"No, we'd have said it right away," Philip answered.

"Then is it any less important to tell God thank you because three times a day He supplies delicious meals for us? He made the food to grow, and He provided us with the money to buy it."

"I guess you're right," said Philip. "But why can't other people see that? Why do we have to be different?"

"I know how you feel," said Mother. "As a young person, I was very self-conscious too, and I found it difficult to pray when others were watching. But I came to see that what God thinks is more important than what people think. God is the One who provided the food. And if others see me thanking Him, perhaps they will be reminded that God has provided for them too. I began to see that praying in a restaurant is an opportunity, not a chore."

"I never thought of it that way," Philip admitted.

"There might be a few people, like those boys last evening, who laugh about your praying, but you may be surprised how many others will respect you," Mother added.

"That reminds me of several songs," said Daddy. " 'This Little Light of Mine' and 'Dare to Be a Daniel.' Which shall we sing first?"

237

" 'This Little Light of Mine,' " said Priscilla eagerly. She liked the motions.

Almost before they knew it, it was lunchtime.

"We made it to Scranton at just the right time," Father said. "And here's a restaurant that looks just fine for a hungry family of five."

This time when they prayed before lunch, Philip didn't look around. He bowed his head and sincerely thanked the Lord for the food.

They were nearly finished with their lunch when a well-dressed elderly couple stopped at their booth. "You have such a nice family." The gentleman smiled. "We have been observing you, and it brought back memories of my own childhood. You prayed before you ate. Your children sit quietly and speak respectfully." The man's eyes grew misty. "It's how things used to be when we were children."

"Thank you," Daddy replied. "We love the Lord and simply want to follow Him and train our children in His ways. Do you follow Jesus?"

The elderly man hesitated, then replied, "Well, we go to church regularly, but . . . let's put it this way: I've been more successful in business than in religion. Seeing your family helps me think about my priorities."

Daddy reached into his shirt pocket and pulled out a Gospel tract. "Here's something you may enjoy reading," he said.

"Oh, thank you," replied the man. "I will read it. And since you have given me something—" he reached and picked up the meal receipt lying next to Daddy's plate. "You won't be offended, will you? You have given us the pleasure of seeing a Christian family; I'd like the additional pleasure of paying for your meal."

"Oh, thank you kindly," Daddy said. "But I—"

"Never mind," the elderly man waved off any objection. "I'm wealthy and count this a privilege."

"Children, what do you say?" asked Father.

"Thank you," chorused the children.

"You are very welcome," said the couple as they moved on. "Enjoy your holidays."

"What do you think, Philip?" Daddy asked when they were again in the car. "Should we let our light shine?"

Philip smiled broadly, then added, "I hope they learn to know Jesus."

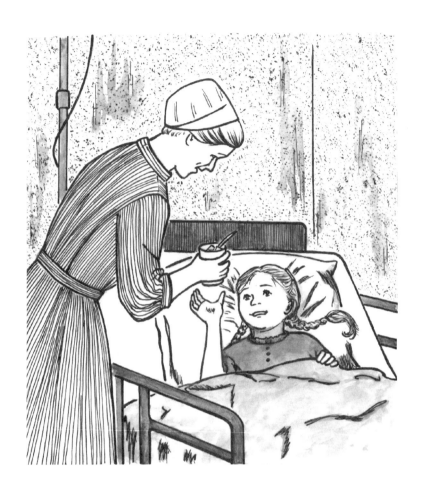

47. What's an Appendectomy?

Lisa clutched her tummy. "Oh, oh, oh, it hurts so!" she moaned. "Go tell Mother I'm sick," she told her eight-year-old sister Lori who was just getting awake from a good night's rest.

Lori stretched and yawned. She wasn't in any great

hurry because apparently Mother was letting them sleep in. Lori wasn't about to be hurried.

"Lori, ple-e-ease go!" begged Lisa. "I mean it—it really hurts!"

Lori didn't need any more begging. One look at Lisa and she was convinced that her ten-year-old sister really was sick. She bounded downstairs to call Mother.

"What seems to be the trouble?" asked Mother as she came to Lisa's bedside.

"My tummy. It hurts! Right here," she said as she placed her hand on her right side. Tears began to trickle down Lisa cheeks. "I don't want to cry, Mother, but it really does hurt *so* much."

After Mother consulted with Daddy, they decided to have Lisa see Doctor Montgomery. Mother helped her get dressed because the pain in Lisa's tummy was getting worse instead of better. Then Mother gave Lori last minute instructions about taking care of little Leslie. "Daddy is in the shop if you need him," added Mother as she closed the door.

When they arrived at Doctor Montgomery's office, the nurse took them into an examination room promptly. She checked Lisa's temperature and asked a lot of questions. Then she got a nightie and told Lisa to put it on and lie on the examining table. "Doctor Montgomery will be in shortly," she added as she left the room.

"Mother, do you think he'll be able to help me?" asked Lisa. "I don't want to complain, but—"

Doctor Montgomery entered, and Lisa never finished what she was saying.

"Hello, Lisa. Let's see . . . your chart says you're ten years old. Right?"

"Yes," answered Lisa.

"Now let's take a look here to see what's 'ouching' you.

241

Does it hurt when I press here? Here? Here?" he asked as he pressed different places on Lisa's tummy. Then he hit *the* spot. "Sorry, I didn't mean to hurt you. I think I know what your problem is. You may get dressed now."

Lisa managed to slip on her clothes while Mother and Doctor Montgomery were talking in the next room. The door was open a bit but Lisa didn't bother listening to their conversation much, though she did hear Doctor Montgomery saying, "She'll probably need an appendectomy."

Appendectomy! What's that? thought Lisa. *Whatever it is, I sure hope it helps.*

Shortly, Mother and Lisa were heading home, at least Lisa thought so.

"Lisa," said Mother, "Doctor Montgomery says he thinks your problem is your appendix. That's a little duct in your stomach that's sick. He wants you to go to the hospital and have an operation to remove your appendix. I'm taking you there now."

Lisa heard no more. *Hospital? Me in the hospital!* she thought. *No, I don't want to go there even though I feel bad. Be there alone? Alone in a big hospital? But Mother's taking me . . . so she'll be there with me. If she's there it won't be so bad maybe. If only I'll feel better.* Her thoughts continued to race until they reached the hospital.

Before long nurses and doctors were busy caring for Lisa. They gave her shots. They took tests. But all the while Lisa's tummy hurt more and more. She was eager to have this appendectomy, or whatever they called it, if it would help her feel better. Shortly she was given a shot that made her very sleepy.

Hours passed but Lisa was not aware of it, for she was fast asleep. The doctors had removed her appendix, and now she heard people calling her name.

"Lisa, your operation's over now. Are you awake? You're in the recovery room," Mother was saying. "Everything went okay."

Later when Lisa was more awake and in her own room, she could hardly believe it when Mother said, "It's eight o'clock in the evening and visiting hours are over. I'll need to go home now. I hope you sleep real well and do what the nurses tell you. They'll take good care of you. Daddy and I will be in tomorrow morning to see you." She planted a kiss on Lisa's cheek, turned to leave, and then added, "Remember Jesus is with you."

Lisa managed to wave a good-bye and give Mother a smile. But when she heard Mother's footsteps disappear down the hallway, she couldn't choke back the tears any longer. One, then another, and another slid down and dampened her pillow. *Here I am. All alone in a big hospital and there isn't one person I know here.* Lisa's thoughts raced and the tears dripped on and on.

A gray-haired, smiling lady wearing a blue-striped uniform entered. "Hello. I see your name is Lisa. I have some ice for you. Here, you may sip on a few ice chips." She hummed softly as she poured ice into a paper cup. She handed the cup of ice and a spoon to Lisa.

"Thank you," said Lisa.

"Oh, you're quite welcome. I'm a volunteer here, and I enjoy seeing and talking with the patients." Then she went humming on her way to help the next patient.

For the moment Lisa forgot about herself and thought of the cheery lady. *What was the tune she was humming?* wondered Lisa. *I'm sure it's a song Mother sings sometimes.* Lisa hummed a bit trying to recall the tune. *Now I have it!* she thought. *"God Will Take Care of You." Mother sings it often.*

243

Lisa tried to recall the words of the song. They seemed to comfort her. She thought of Jesus and how He called the children to Himself long ago. How comforting to know He loved her too, and that He could and would take care of her! Then as she thought about Jesus, she didn't feel all alone anymore. *Tonight I feel like praying and talking to Jesus. I guess other times I just say words instead of really praying.*

Realizing that she could not get out of bed to kneel, Lisa closed her eyes and opened her heart to God right there in her hospital bed.

"Dear God, thank You that You will take care of me. I'm glad I don't need to feel so alone because You are here watching over me.

"Thank You for the kind nurses and doctors. And for that lady that brought the ice chips.

"Take care of Mother, Daddy, Lori, and Leslie.

"If You will, please heal my tummy, so I can go home again.

"And God, this morning I didn't know what an appendectomy was. Now I know. But I learned something even more important. I learned You will take care of me wherever I am. Thank You.

"In Jesus' name I pray. Amen."

Then Lisa drifted off to sleep.

48. Amos's Trip to the Mill

A Story From Long Ago

Amos, impatient Amos, popped several grains of corn into his mouth and chewed them. Not that he enjoyed the flavor, but it did give him something to do.

The weather was cloudy, damp, and cold—typical conditions before a January snow. All of nature seemed to be asleep except for an occasional chickadee flitting about the underbrush.

Why did I come along? wondered Amos, as he pulled his patched wrap closer about his neck. *I usually can hardly wait until it's my turn to go along to Zook's Mill. But not today.* He knew his brothers were probably skating on the frozen creek by now. They had chores to do, but as soon as they were done they'd promptly grab their skates. And here he was. Going at a snail's pace to the mill.

Amos glanced at his father sitting beside him on the spring wagon seat. His cheeks were red from the cold, and he was deep in thought. He held Shorty's reins loosely allowing Shorty to proceed at his usual slow gait.

Amos's toes started tapping on the wagon bed. The taps, however, were not in rhythm with Shorty's slow clip-clops. Amos's toes tapped twice as fast. He was becoming more and more bored.

Once more he glanced toward Father. Father was a man of few words, not given to idle conversation. Deeply loved by his family, he was also highly respected. A God-fearing man, Father was a through-the-week Christian, not merely a Sunday churchgoer. The Christian life was all-important to him, and he tried to teach his children likewise. Their words and actions were at all times to be above reproach.

Amos stuck his hands deeper into his pockets. *We're only at the covered bridge? It never took so long to get to the mill before,* he decided. *Now we have that long hill ahead of us yet. Maybe we should change Shorty's name to Molasses, as slow and stiff as he is today. Wish Father would get a snappier horse or at least giddy-up Shorty more. Maybe if I had the reins I could get him galloping.*

But Amos didn't dare verbalize any of these thoughts. He appeared content on the outside, but inwardly his impatience could hardly be contained. *When will we get to the miller so he can roast and grind our bag of corn and we can go home!*

Amos was seemingly the only one who noticed that Shorty's pace had become even slower as he trudged up the gravel hill.

"I could walk that fast!" Amos finally exclaimed.

Several seconds elapsed. "Whoa, Shorty," called Father as he pulled on the reins.

Shorty followed his command and came to a halt.

Father looked at Amos, and Amos knew without a further word from Father what he had to do.

Amos jumped from the spring wagon and started walking up the steep, long hill. Meanwhile Shorty transported Father to the mill.

By the time Amos's cold stiff legs got him to the mill, he had learned the hard way the meaning of the verse, "Let your yea be yea; and your nay, nay."

49. The Boot Buckle

"Oh, look! It's snowing! Hurray!" cheered Timothy with his dimpled face pressed against the cold windowpane. Snow brought excitement, and six-year-old Timothy was ready anytime for fun and adventure.

Immediately upon hearing the word "snow," his little

sister, Julia, forgot all about the marble roller. The last blue and white marble made its noisy trek to the bottom, but Julia was watching something more fascinating—the snowflakes. "Oh, oh, look at that one!" squealed Julia as she stretched on her tiptoes to peer out the window. "A flake mashed on the—"

"No, it didn't mash! It splashed," corrected Timothy. He felt it was his responsibility as a six-year-old to correct his little sister's speech. After all, he was almost three whole years older than she. *She is such a baby,* he thought to himself. *Silly and always wanders after me. Often spoils my fun too. Wish I had a brother my age, instead of a baby sister.* Secretly, however, he did enjoy being her hero.

Julia didn't even notice the correction. She was occupied with snowflake watching when Mother came into the playroom and nearly collided with Timothy. He was darting toward the doorway.

"Mamma, may I go outside to play in the snow?"

"No, not now. Perhaps after supper you may awhile. Right now I'd like you to pick up all these toys and put your puzzle away. Daddy will soon be in. So get the things away, then tidy up. Wash your hands and comb your hair. Julia, that includes you too."

Timothy felt like pouting. Pick up toys when there are snowflakes flying? But he had learned the hard way to obey. When Mamma said something she meant it. Obedience was important at the Millers' home, so Timothy set to work.

"Julia, hurry up! Why are you so poky? Put the doll away!" Timothy directed.

"What is a poky?" asked Julia as she ambled slowly to the toy chest. She didn't seem overly concerned that the floor still had toys strewn all about. She was more eager to say new words she heard coming from Timothy's lips.

"A poky is a . . . a . . . a. Oh, forget it!" retorted Timothy. "Maybe I'll tell you sometime."

"Supper!" called Mamma.

Suppertime, a highlight of the day for the whole family, was soon past. The clean dishes were neatly stacked in the cupboard.

"Now, Mamma, may I go outside awhile?" Timothy asked.

"Is it still snowing?" asked Mamma.

Papa Miller answered that question. "It certainly is. But I'd say let them bundle up and go outside for awhile. They can see with the yard light, and a little fresh air won't hurt them. That will also give us the chance to work at the desk. There are bills here to be paid."

Clapping her hands, Julia raced to the closet for boots. She always had to work hard to slip them on, but she managed.

"Oh, must Julia go along with me? Then I have to watch her," groaned Timothy. He had his own ideas, and his little sister didn't fit into his plans.

"If you want to complain about playing with Julia, perhaps it would be wiser to send you to bed promptly," stated Papa.

Timothy said no more. He knew Papa would carry out this suggestion if he muttered again.

Timothy managed to close most of the buckles on his boots. There were one, two, three, four, five on each boot. But the bottom one on the left boot didn't want to close, and Timothy was in too big a hurry to mess with it. After all, it really didn't matter. The snow wouldn't come in.

Timothy clump-clumped to the side door. There he

impatiently waited for Julia. He kept turning the doorknob and staring at her with his hurry-up-you-slowpoke look.

But as soon as they were frolicking in the snow, big brother Timothy forgot to be unhappy with Julia. In fact, it was more fun because she was there. Together they planned a surprise for Papa.

"Julia, let's clean Papa's windshield on the car. It has lots of snow on it. We'll climb on the hood and brush it off. Then he won't have to tomorrow morning. Won't he be surprised?"

Of course, Julia cooperated. First they climbed on the bumper, and then slippy, slippy-slide, they got onto the hood. They could not see the new paint job on the car because it was all snow-covered. And the windshield was soon uncovered. Timothy and Julia used the ice scraper and swish, swished the snow to the ground. First the driver's side, then they slid across to the passenger's side.

"Now, let's play in the yard so Mamma and Papa won't see us here. Remember not to tell them. It's a surprise," warned Timothy.

"Mmm-huh," she agreed, as she slid off the hood and landed flat-out on the snow-covered ground. Fortunately the fall didn't hurt much.

Timothy crawled to one side, then nimbly jumped to the driveway.

"Children, time for bed," called Mamma's voice. "Take those boots off in the laundry before you come in."

Timothy and Julia smiled happily in the laundry as they tugged to remove their boots. They were happy the surprise job was completed. Soon they both were nestled in their warm, cozy beds. Outside snowflakes continued to blanket the earth.

Next morning Papa left for Wright's store before the children were up. He hadn't noticed their good deed. More snow had hidden their work. The snow was now blizzard size.

Timothy and Julia slept late, and Papa returned with groceries while they were eating breakfast. No one mentioned a clean, swept windshield. Even Timothy and Julia were thinking too much about the snow to remember the windshield.

The blizzard brought fun, hard work, and excitement to the Miller home. The snowbound days passed quickly and life soon resumed its normal activities.

But one day Papa came in with a puzzled expression. "Would anyone know what made the big scratch across the hood of the car? I just got it back two weeks ago from the body shop; now it's all scratched up." Papa seemed unhappy. His voice was stern.

"No; I don't," answered Mamma.

"It wasn't me," Timothy quipped.

"Not me, either. I can't reach it," stated Julia.

"Well, something scraped it—clear across the hood. There are several little scratches too."

"Which side?" questioned Mamma.

"Both driver's and passenger's side."

"Timothy, did you throw anything on the hood of the car? Or push a stick across it?"

"No, I didn't," Timothy promptly replied.

"Did you climb up on the car recently?"

"No—" Then Timothy remembered. Fear gripped his heart. The windshield! "Oh . . . yeah . . . Julia and I were wanting to surprise you. That night the snow came and we were playing outside, we climbed up on the hood. We cleaned off the windshield for you. So you could see to drive. But . . . we didn't scratch the hood. I don't think so, anyway."

"You had your boots on," said Papa. "Your boots have buckles."

The boot buckle! Timothy had not buckled that last one.

"Do you think that's what it was?" Mamma asked.

"I—I—didn't buckle one," Timothy confessed.

"Did you slide on the car hood?" asked Papa.

"Yes, to get the whole windshield clean."

"I'm glad you wanted to help me, Timothy, but you must not climb on the hood of cars. Boots and shoes can scratch the paint."

"I didn't know that," said Timothy.

"And I won't punish you this time," replied Papa. "But don't forget. Paint can be scratched. You must also not throw rocks or sticks, or rub them on a car. This is a lesson you had better remember for a long time, Timothy."

And Timothy did.

50. The Prize at Dentist Groff's Office

"Carolyn Shelly," called Marge, Dentist Groff's nurse. "Come with me, please." She flashed a friendly smile at Carolyn.

Carolyn slid from the high settee and handed Mother

the magazine she had been looking at. Marge picked up Carolyn's dental record at the desk, then headed back the hallway. Carolyn followed.

Carolyn had mixed feelings about coming here to Dentist Groff's office. On the bad side was the teeth cleaning, the shot to numb the feeling in her gums, and, ugh, the drilling. Plus she detested the sound of the filling being pressed into the freshly drilled hole. That sound was similar to hearing chalk squeak across a blackboard, except worse.

But there was a good side too. The friendliness and the prize at the end.

"In here, Carolyn," Marge told her. "I'll clean your teeth first of all. Then Doctor Groff will take care of the cavity we found the last time you were here."

Carolyn followed her into the cheery room. She paused momentarily to look at the wall decorations. This new office was so much prettier than the old one. Large animal pictures greeted the visitors.

"How do you like our animals?" asked Marge. "We planned this room especially for our little friends that come. We hope you enjoy them as much as we do."

Carolyn's face told Marge she did. Why, there was a tall giraffe in an awkward position trying to brush his teeth. The toothbrush handle was gigantically long. The elephant on the wall had a tube of toothpaste wrapped in his trunk and he was trying hard to get it onto the toothbrush. Long toothpaste strips on the ground showed he had missed.

Over there was the cutest thing yet. A mother monkey was brushing a baby monkey's teeth. And next to the monkey family was an octopus all tangled up in dental floss.

"Carolyn, will you sit on this chair, please? I'll give

you a free ride." When Carolyn was seated, Marge pushed a button somewhere, and Carolyn felt the chair rising. "There, that's fine," Marge said, and she brought the right arm of the chair down to the examining position and clipped a napkin about Carolyn's neck.

If I have to go the dentist, I'm glad to come here, decided Carolyn. She liked the cheery room. And Marge. Her kind way of talking helped to make the visit more enjoyable.

"How old are you?" asked Marge.

"Nine," answered Carolyn.

Marge chatted while she cleaned Carolyn's teeth. Carolyn grunted yes and no answers to her questions. She couldn't talk with her mouth filled with a little mirror plus other cleaning instruments. Then Marge gave Carolyn a small cup of water to rinse her mouth.

"Hello, Carolyn. How are you today?" asked Dentist Groff's deep voice.

"I'm fine."

"I can see you are. If I had your pretty pigtails I would be too." He grabbed the right plait and jerked it. "May I have one?" he asked teasingly.

"No," Carolyn answered.

"Why not?"

" 'Cause they're mine," she said.

"But I don't have any and you have two. That's not fair." Dentist Groff acted terribly disappointed.

Carolyn giggled. He was always so funny. She couldn't help but like him.

The shot and the drilling weren't as bad as she had feared. Time passed quickly while Dentist Groff worked, and in a short time he was done.

"Now you're all finished. What do you say, Marge? Do you think she deserves a prize?" asked Dentist Groff.

"Yes, she does! May I have the privilege of giving it to her?" laughed Marge.

"I suppose you may do that. But let her choose which one she wants," Dentist Groff stated.

Marge opened the cupboard door and gently lifted a box from the shelf. Carolyn was very curious about what it contained.

Sometimes the prize was a pencil or a pack of cherry sugar-free gum. *What will it be?* wondered Carolyn.

She didn't need to wonder long. Marge held the box invitingly in front of her. There were rows and rows of sparkling rings. Only one had been taken out so far. They were all tucked into the slots in the velvet-covered box bottom. Some were especially for boys and others especially for girls. Others could be used by either. Some had pictures of animals on them. There was a variety of colors and a few looked like real diamonds.

Which one shall I take? wondered Carolyn. *Which one would most impress the other girls at school? Of course, I'd never tell Mother or Daddy I have a finger ring. They disapprove of wearing jewelry because the Bible teaches us not to wear ornaments. But they wouldn't know if I'd carry it in my coat pocket.*

Carolyn was almost ready to select one. But she just couldn't decide. Did she want the blue-green one, which looked the prettiest, or the gold that would match her brown, flowered school dress? She hesitated one moment longer, her eyes fixed on the sparkling contents of the box.

Marge is waiting. I must decide. But in the back of her mind she knew it would never work to have a finger ring in her home.

"No, thank you. I don't believe I care for any," Carolyn blurted out. She almost surprised herself. Her cheeks were hot, and even her knees felt a bit weak as she followed Marge to the receptionist's desk. Would Marge mind that she didn't take a prize?

But Marge seemed as pleasant as ever when Mother came over from the waiting room to pay the bill. "Carolyn was a very good patient, Mrs. Shelly," remarked Marge as she placed her hand on Carolyn's shoulder. Turning toward the waiting room for the next patient, she added, "Carolyn, don't eat too much candy till I see you again."

No, Marge doesn't seem to mind that I refused, thought Carolyn, as she waited for Mother.

Carolyn's cheeks still felt hot, but she was calmer now.

"Come, Carolyn," Mother said as she slipped the checkbook into her purse. She smiled warmly at her daughter. But Mother didn't realize the real prize Carolyn won during the visit to Dentist Groff.

51. Sheryl and Her Scissors Lesson

"Snip, snip, snip," went Sheryl's scissors. They opened and closed, cutting jagged edges around a picture of a teddy bear.

Admiringly Sheryl looked at her latest cutout, then stacked it with the others she planned to paste in the book she was making. She loved playing with the new, blunt-edge scissors Mother and Daddy had given to her yesterday for her sixth birthday.

"Always remember to put the scissors away when you're done with them," Mother had instructed when Sheryl opened her package containing paste, paper, and a scissors.

"I will," promised Sheryl. "Thank you so much!" She was so happy to have scissors of her own.

Her older sisters, Sheila and Sharon, who went to school, were allowed to use Mother's scissors. But Sheryl wasn't old enough.

"Now I can cut too!" exclaimed Sheryl.

"Yes," smiled Daddy. "But remember what Mother said about putting them away. If little Shannon would get them, he could hurt himself," warned Daddy.

"Oh, I will," answered Sheryl, certain that she would *always* do that.

The following day while the older girls were in school and Shannon, who was almost three, was taking a nap, Mother was sewing.

Sheryl was busy cutting and pasting. "What are you making, Mother?" asked Sheryl.

"A dress for myself," answered Mother. "I hope to have it finished for the wedding we're invited to on Saturday.

"Almost done," stated Mother, as she got up from the sewing machine. She folded the nearly completed dress and hung it across the back of her chair.

"I hear Shannon," said Sheryl.

"So do I," said Mother. "I'll go upstairs and get him. While I'm up, I'll put the folded wash into the drawer."

"I'll stay downstairs and cut out some more pictures," decided Sheryl. One after another was snipped from the catalog pages.

Screech. Screech. The brakes of the school bus

announced Sheila and Sharon had arrived at the end of the lane.

Quickly Sheryl grabbed her coat and scarf and ran to meet her sisters. She was always glad to hear what they had to say about school. Of course they were full of questions about the day's activities at home. Sheryl filled them in on that.

Soon Mother was bustling about the kitchen getting supper on the stove. Sheila and Sharon were busy with their assigned chores while Shannon contented himself in the sewing room.

Sheryl picked up the paper scraps and put her cutouts into her keepsake box.

When Daddy got home, Mother called, "Supper's ready." Sheila and Sharon helped dish up the food, and Sheryl scrambled onto her stool awaiting the delicious supper.

"I'll get Shannon," Daddy volunteered.

"He's in the sewing room," said Mother as she put the meat loaf on the platter.

"Mother, come here!" Daddy's voice called. It certainly didn't sound like his usual tone of voice.

"Oh, no!" the girls heard Mother say. "How did he do it?"

The three girls hurried to the sewing room in time to hear Daddy say, "With these," as he held up Sheryl's scissors.

How bad Sheryl felt! There stood Mother surveying her new dress with several holes gashed into the front of the skirt. Disappointment was written across Mother's face.

"I'm sorry! I'm sorry I didn't put the scissors away," sobbed Sheryl as she rushed over to Mother.

"Sheryl," said Daddy, "I know it was Shannon who

made the holes. But it was you who left the scissors lie. You did not obey us. We told you to always put them away. The Bible says, 'Children, obey your parents.'"

"I know," sobbed Sheryl. "I forgot. I'm very sorry I didn't obey."

"I'll forgive you," answered Mother softly. "Perhaps I have enough fabric left to cut another piece for the skirt."

"Sheryl, I'm glad to see you're sorry," said Daddy. "But, you go and lay these scissors in my desk drawer. You will not use them until I give them back to you. You will need to remember to obey your parents. Even if you don't know why we say so, we expect you to obey. In addition to cutting Mother's dress, Shannon could have cut himself."

Sheryl looked at Daddy and nodded her tear-stained face. Then she deposited her treasured scissors into Daddy's desk drawer.

"Let's eat now," said Mother.

"Yes," agreed Daddy. "I'm hungry."

Although Sheryl wasn't hungry, she slid onto her stool. As the family bowed their heads for silent prayer, Sheryl said, "Thank You for our food. And I'm sorry I disobeyed. Help me remember next time. Thank You for keeping Shannon safe. In Jesus' name. Amen."

She felt better now and actually enjoyed Mother's meat loaf. But she knew she would never forget the scissors lesson.

52. "Happy Birthday, Cindy!"

"Mother, Mother, what time is it? How soon will the mailman come?" Cindy asked.

Cindy could hardly wait. Twenty minutes was such a long time. She was sure there would be at least four cards for her. Today was her birthday! Grandma Wilson, Cousin Anne, Aunt Rhoda, and her good friend Susie, who lived next door, would never forget her birthday.

Cindy sat right inside the window where she could see Mr. Baley's car as soon as it rounded the corner.

"You know it won't be your birthday for two years yet." Mother's eyes twinkled.

Cindy grinned. She had been born on February 29, a day that comes once every four years. The other years, she celebrated her birthday on February 28, the last day of the month.

"February is the shortest month of the year," Cindy mused. "Why does it seem like such a long month?"

"Probably for several reasons," replied Mother.

"Like what?" Cindy asked.

"Your birthday for one," replied Mother. "You think about it all month long, and the more you think about it, the longer the time seems. But school is another reason. In January and February there are no breaks. It's wintertime, and by the end of February, we are all wishing for spring."

"It's such a long, boring month," said Cindy. "Oh! There's the mailman." She grabbed her jacket and raced out the door to the mailbox.

Yes, there were cards—one, two, three, four envelopes with her name on them. She dashed back to the house shouting, "Mother, look!" She waved the four cards.

Then she tore them open and read and admired each colorful greeting.

Mother wiped her hands on the towel and came to sit beside Cindy. She read each of the cards too. None were alike. As Mother finished reading, she asked, "Cindy, do you know what each of these people wished you?"

"A happy birthday!" Cindy promptly replied.

"They wished you more than that, didn't they?" Mother asked.

Cindy thought hard. "Oh, I know. They wished me a happy year."

"Right," Mother said. "But Cindy, what does being happy really mean? Is it getting everything you want? Is it getting out of wiping the dishes because it's your special day?"

Cindy didn't know what to say. It was nice to get cards, and she really didn't enjoy drying dishes. She was about to say yes, but Mother went on. "Try to think of the times you have been most happy. I mean really happy, not only having fun and enjoying yourself."

"Oh, I remember the time I gave my new blue sweater to Jane Black because she didn't have any. And last week, Mother, when I surprised you by cleaning up the kitchen while you were in town."

As Cindy kept thinking, she thought of more times she had been extra happy.

"Cindy, did you think about it that most of the times you have been especially happy, you were doing something for someone else? Isn't it wonderful how loving others, caring about them, and sharing with them in turn makes us happy?"

"But is it wrong to look forward to my birthday and enjoy my birthday cards?" Cindy asked.

"No. Certainly not, Cindy," Mother replied. "As long as you aren't all taken up with yourself. As long as you are appreciative. You are one year older today. I was thinking about how you can make this coming year a happy one. You are growing. This year you will be able to help others more than you did last year. Jesus said, 'It is more blessed to give than to receive.' And if you think about happiness that way, you will be a happy

265

person all year—even in February."

Cindy smiled. "I guess it's too late for this February, but I'll try to remember next year this time."

"Happy birthday, Cindy—I hope you have a happy year!"

Art Acknowledgements

Artists:

David Miller	Spring section and page 208
Michelle Beidler	Summer and Fall sections
Treda Beachy	Winter section except page 208

Front cover photographs:

Center: Virginia Swartzendruber

Clockwise, starting at top left:

> Virginia Swartzendruber
> Kevin and Bethany Shank
> Dogwood Ridge Photography
> Virginia Swartzendruber
> Verna M. Martin
> Sara Miller
> Rachel Friesen
> Kevin and Bethany Shank
>   and Verna M. Martin
> Kevin and Bethany Shank
> Dogwood Ridge Photography
> Verna M. Martin
> Kevin and Bethany Shank
> Verna M. Martin
> Dogwood Ridge Photography

Back cover photograph:

> Images © 1997 PhotoDisc, Inc.

Christian Light Publications, Inc., is a nonprofit conservative Mennonite publishing company providing Christ-centered, Biblical literature in a variety of forms including Gospel tracts, books, Sunday school materials, summer Bible school materials, and a full curriculum for Christian day schools and homeschools.

For more information at no obligation or for spiritual help, please write to us at:

Christian Light Publications, Inc.
P. O. Box 1212
Harrisonburg, VA 22801-1212